Perry could hear Tarquin's voice...

The same voice that had often penetrated her sleep. Now it was real, and hands that she had thought never to feel again held her as she fell against him in the rain-swept night. She could see him in the car headlights—the same Tarquin she had secretly married five years earlier!

"I know you never wanted to see me again," Perry stammered, "but I'll leave as soon as we've talked."

"Who are you?" Tarquin demanded. "Should I know you?"

It was as though Perry had stepped into an elevator shaft when she had expected solid ground. How could she tell this man who regarded her as a stranger that she was his wife? Surely he was just pretending....

Or had he really forgotten her?

OTHER
Harlequin Romances
by GWEN WESTWOOD

Many of these titles are available at your local bookseller.

For a free catalogue listing all available Harlequin Romances,
send your name and address to:

HARLEQUIN READER SERVICE,
M.P.O. Box 707, Niagara Falls, N.Y. 14302
Canadian address: Stratford, Ontario, Canada N5A 6W2

Forgotten Bride

by

GWEN WESTWOOD

Harlequin Books

TORONTO • LONDON • LOS ANGELES • AMSTERDAM
SYDNEY • HAMBURG • PARIS • STOCKHOLM • ATHENS • TOKYO

Original hardcover edition published in 1980
by Mills & Boon Limited

ISBN 0-373-02363-4

Harlequin edition published October 1980

Printed in the U.S.A.

CHAPTER ONE

'WAS I crazy to insist on coming back?' Perry Vaughan asked herself as she left the small gas station and headed straight towards the gathering storm clouds.

'Going far, *nkosizane*?' the African attendant had asked her. 'Plenty bad weather coming over that way.'

At her call he had come dancing out of his shaky little shelter into the high hot wind, clicking his fingers, singing some snatch of tune, oblivious of the heat and the gritty dust that swirled around the untarred road, as he cheerfully filled the tank, measured the oil with a dipstick and sprayed cleaning fluid on to the smeared windscreen.

'Look like you came from a far way. Where's you heading, young madam?'

'I'm going to Lion's Rock Game Park,' she told him.

'Mr Winslow's place?' There was a doubtful note in the voice of the attendant. 'Mr Winslow doesn't have many visitors to his reserve no more. Know what he told me one day? Said to me animals are more important than people. Strange man, that one. Where you come from, *nkosizane*?'

'I've come from England.'

'England? So far? Madam, you sure are a long way from home,' he told her, his African accent overlaid by his idea of how the cowboys sounded in his favourite American movies.

'I sure am,' she agreed laughingly as she drove away.

But when she was alone again on the dusty road, she

didn't feel so much like laughing. The meeting with the cheery pump attendant had made her feel at home once more in this vast untamed part of Africa, but nothing else did. What had happened to it? It was the same and yet not the same. Had she imagined all that wild loveliness that had held her so enchanted five years ago? Had it all been part of a girlish dream? The dust from the road blew in red clouds around the little car, seeping through to the interior, covering her light beige slacks with a thin film of grit, dulling the shining blonde of her hair, irritating the damp hollow between her breasts where the cream silk shirt was loosely buttoned. She had been driving all day and it would be heavenly to have a hot bath followed by a cool shower, she thought.

Even above the noise of the engine and the howl of the wind against the car doors, she could hear the thunder as it roared like a questing lion, and lightning, as yet still distant on the horizon, flashed in jagged streaks. Great dark clouds piled up in the azure sky as if they were the result of an atomic explosion. The lightning outlined the flat thorn trees in the seemingly endless landscape and, every now and again, the pale green bark of a fever tree looked even more livid in this eerie light. A troop of baboons loped across the road and disappeared into the trees while the leader stayed by the roadside, his ugly face turned menacingly towards Perry, and she remembered, goodness knows how, that Africans believed a night of storm belonged to the Abatakadi, male wizards who rode backwards upon baboons across the threatening sky.

Her girlhood memories of Africa had not included storms. No, she had remembered a place luminous with heavenly gold light like some vision of Paradise. And that other time here had been the nearest to heaven she had ever known until those terrible final hours. Something deep inside her quivered with fear. This wasn't how she had planned it, an arrival in stormswept darkness. She tried to ignore the feeling. Even if you had arrived in brilliant sunshine, she told herself, there would still have had to be some kind of confrontation. You knew that all along. Storm or sunshine, what difference does it make? At the end of the long weary journey, you know that you have to face Tarquin Winslow.

That was why Sinclair had tried to persuade her that she should let him negotiate with Tarquin from a distance of eight thousand miles.

'There's absolutely no need for you to meet this man, Perdita,' he had said.

He always called her by her full name, though no one else ever used it. But with his precise kind of mind, he hated abbreviations.

'He has done enough damage to your life already. He behaved like a brute all the way through. I hate the very thought of your meeting this creature again.'

Dear Sinclair, he was just what she needed, Perry thought. Her sister Wendy thought he was not very exciting, but what did she want with excitement? He was ready to protect, love and cherish her, ready to make a safe kind of life for her. And yet she had insisted on coming on her mission alone. She couldn't even imagine Sinclair in Africa, much less meeting Tarquin. Sinclair was so suave, so urbane. He belonged to a smooth civilised life in big cities, and, when she married him, always provided he asked her, of course, she would have an easy, luxurious life with no rough edges, very different indeed from the life she could have expected with Tarquin.

Considering his dislike of excessive drama in his life, Sinclair had taken her revelation remarkably well, she thought, and he had been willing to arrange everything through business associates in Africa, willing to smooth out the tangle so that she need have no part in it. Why, therefore, had she been so foolish as to insist on coming herself?

'He didn't even reply to the letters I sent at first,' she explained to Sinclair, 'so how can I expect that he would reply now, when five years have passed?'

'There are other ways of finding out the true position, trust me. I'll soon get it sorted out,' Sinclair declared. 'My poor, sweet girl! I hate to think of what you must have suffered at the hands of that brute.'

It's true that I did suffer more than I could ever make anyone understand, Perry thought. But there was joy too, such heavenly joy! I could never tell Sinclair that. Those few days of my secret marriage belonged to some enchanted world that I've never again entered. And afterwards there was silence, blank horrible nothingness until at last I realised that I'd imagined it all, that the heavenly joy had been all on my side, and that all he had ever wanted was an easy conquest, only I was so young and innocent that he had to set up this pretence so that I truly believed I was his wife.

'In my heart,' she told Sinclair, 'I know that the marriage was not legal. How could it have been? A small chapel in the wilderness, an African minister, everything so secret. I was only seventeen and the two black witnesses could neither read nor write. Even the ring....'

But she didn't explain to Sinclair about the ring or the fact that she still had it hidden away in a small compartment of her jewel case, a tiny ring made of twisted gold and elephant hair. That at least had been real, a small piece of Africa even if it had not been a conventional wedding ring.

'I think you're probably right,' Sinclair agreed. 'This man can't have had the slightest intention of contracting a legal marriage. He just took advantage of your youth and innocence to get what he wanted. Otherwise how could he have behaved as he did? Why did he desert you so soon without even acknowledging the marriage? All the same, we must get it sorted out before we can make any plans for your future. You can't have this shadow hanging over your life for ever. But I do wish you would let me send some-one to do it for you.'

'No, Sinclair, I must go myself,' Perry had vowed adamantly.

So that was why she was driving through this wilderness, and, as the dark clouds, slit by metallic flashes, were tossed across the high vault of the wide African sky, she won-dered again what had made her choose the hard way. Ad-mit it, she told herself, you're terrified of meeting him again, Tarquin, whom at seventeen you really imagined was the love of your life. No, I didn't imagine it. He was my first love, even if I wasn't his. Oh, no, there must have been many girls before me. Perhaps I was different. My innocence was a novelty to him.

But what will he do? What will his reaction be when he sees me again? And with quivering senses she thought, will he laugh, mocking laughter, because I've come all this way to find out something that should have been obvious to any-one but an ignorant infatuated girl, that this strange mar-riage was a pretence and that, just as quickly as he'd been attracted to me, he tired of me, so that he didn't want me any more and was glad to let me go?

She remembered suddenly and quite vividly how Tar-quin had looked when he laughed, chestnut head thrown back above the strong column of his throat, brown muscles quivering on the bare chest with its silky pelt of dark hairs, eyes golden as a panther's losing their fierceness now, los-ing their proud reserve in a rare moment of uncomplicated humour. Oh, heavens, why could she remember him so well, and would he still look the same?

The clouds were lower now, blotting out the horizon, yet still the rain held off, but the little car was being tossed by the buffeting wind like a cork in a rough sea. That small gas station, run by Africans, had been the last touch of civilisation in a hundred miles and now there was nothing around her but stretches of wilderness, plains of rough grass dotted with clumps of flat-topped thorn trees. Sometimes in the frequent flashes of lightning, she would glimpse a small group of round thatched huts some miles from the road, but, as she came nearer to the end of her journey, even those disappeared and she knew she was approaching the huge area known as Lion's Rock. It was a private reserve set aside for the conservation of animals where they lived in their natural habitat.

Tarquin's great-grandfather had bought vast tracts of land in the days of the early settlers at the time when animal herds were so numerous as to seem indestructable. But years of wanton killing took their toll and Tarquin's grandfather, wealthy from fortunate mining ventures and wiser than most of his generation, decided to set aside Lion's Rock for the preservation of the dwindling African wild life. Five years ago, Perry's grandfather had been the Winslows' nearest neighbour, owning a farm on the edge of the reserve. Perry had come to stay with them, and that was how it had all happened. The farm no longer existed as a farm, for, after her grandparents' deaths, Tarquin had bought up their land to increase even more the vast reserve.

She had told Sinclair she hoped to be back within the week, but the bad roads and now this foul weather had delayed her. She had hoped to arrive in the middle of the day and maybe journey back to the nearest small town where she could stay for the night. But now this seemed ruled out. She remembered what the pump attendant had said about the fact that Tarquin no longer had many visitors to the reserve. Maybe that was all to the good. If the chalets were not full, she could stay at the rest camp overnight. This was some way from the splendid main house where Tarquin lived, so once her interview was over she could go there and, if she departed early tomorrow, she need not see him again. Sinclair had wanted to write and tell Tarquin she was coming, but she had vehemently refused.

'There's nothing I could put on paper,' she had said.

But she had allowed Sinclair to make discreet enquiries and at least she knew that Tarquin still lived at Lion's Rock. That was all. Of the personal side of his life she knew nothing.

'What if you find he's married?' Wendy, her sister, had asked. She was the only other person who knew about that part of Perry's past life.

'Then I'll know for sure that our marriage was false,' Perry told her.

'I think it's crazy to want to go there yourself. Suppose you find you're still attracted to him?'

'I won't,' said Perry shortly. 'He can mean nothing to me now.'

'How can you be so sure? It doesn't seem to me that you're so passionately in love with Sinclair.'

For some reason Wendy did not seem to like Sinclair, but Perry tried to ignore the fact.

'I don't want passion,' she said now. 'That time in Africa I had enough high excitement and enough disillusionment too to last me a lifetime. With Sinclair I hope to have a calm ordered life. That's what I want now. The other was too painful.'

'A well ordered life sounds pretty dull to me and not your kind of scene at all. I've always envied the exciting things that seem to happen to you. Your talent for photo journalism has led you to some pretty glamorous assignments.'

'Oh, yes, I've been fortunate. If I marry Sinclair I'll have to give all that up, I expect. He won't want a wife with a career.'

'There you are, you see. What did I tell you? You'll soon

get tired of being the perfect hostess and running a gracious home for him. And I'll tell you this much—it seems pretty dicey to me to go out there to Africa and meet Tarquin again if he's as devastating as you said he was.'

'That's nonsense, Wendy. I was only seventeen. He was the first man I'd ever loved. How can I know what he was really like? I'll probably think he's terrible now. My taste in men has changed since those days.'

'It most certainly has,' said Wendy frankly. 'Granted Sinclair is quite good-looking in a frozen kind of way, but he certainly is no sunbronzed game ranger. And even if you were very young, this Tarquin must have had a lot of charm to get you to marry him in secret after you'd only known each other a couple of weeks.'

'Oh, I know it all sounds crazy,' Perry admitted, 'but I suppose I was carried away by the romance of it all. It was wild and completely mad, but I was very young. You know I'd only just left school when I came to stay with the grandparents and I can't describe what an impact Africa made on me, the heavenly climate, the beautiful strange animals in the Reserve, the vast sweep of the deep blue sky, the hot sunlight, and then meeting Tarquin! To any young romantic girl he would have seemed the answer to all her dreams. He was so rugged, so tall, so virile. I was already deeply in love with him when we were flung together on that wilderness trail.'

'The grandparents must have been pretty trusting to let you go alone with him when Gran became ill,' commented Wendy.

'It seems so now, but in a way it's understandable because all the time they regarded me as a child. I suppose in a way I encouraged them to think so. By that time I was so infatuated with Tarquin I'd have done anything to be with him. I longed to be alone with him and if they'd even suspected this they would have tried to prevent it. But they had no idea of it. Every time we met, I was utterly drawn to him, and after he started to kiss me occasionally, I longed with a kind of feverish desire for his touch. He must have realised this, of course. He was so much older and he must have had lots of experience with women.'

'Had he made love to you at all before you were alone together in the wilderness?' asked Wendy.

Perry's wide blue eyes had a far away dreaminess as she looked back across the years.

'Oh, yes. Whenever he came to dinner, if we were left alone he would kiss me and caress me. Oh, Wendy, can you imagine what it was like to be made love to for the first time in such glamorous surroundings? There was the scent of the jasmine, the throb of guitars from the servants' compound, a huge silver moon riding high in a sky of deep azure blue and the shadows of leaves in the darkness where we sat on a cushioned swinging seat. And Tarquin, the most masculine creature I'd ever met. I'd never attracted or been attracted to any man before him, and when he kissed me it was as if I were lost in some enchanted dream.'

Wendy shook her head.

'If it was as heavenly as all that, I still say you shouldn't go back.'

'But, Wendy, it all happened five years ago ... another life. It was very important to me then, but obviously not to him.'

'It's strange that he never even got in touch with you again.'

Perry gave a little bitter laugh.

'Obviously I'd served my purpose. I was carried away by the glamour of the situation, but now I'm five years older and wiser. I'd never be such a fool again.'

'I wonder what would have happened if you hadn't been called back home suddenly?'

'Who can tell? He said everything must be kept a secret,

but he promised he'd come for me as soon as he could arrange it. He never did. I wrote to him, of course—frantic letters. I don't like to think about them, but he never replied. He must just have been glad that I'd gone out of his life so easily.'

Remembering these things had helped her drive through the storm without fear, but now a particularly vivid flash of lightning showed her two large iron gates. She was here already! She remembered them as being always open to welcome visitors, beside them a smiling African guard in a safari suit who wrote down particulars about your car and checked your booking. But now they looked very firmly closed, a heavy linked chain holding the two rusted sides, where a pair of stone lions snarled down from the black basalt pillars on each side.

As she emerged from the car, drops of rain as big as pennies whipped up the dust in front of her and in moments her long blonde hair was dripping and her thin clothes clinging wetly to her body. Lightning ripped the sky and in front of her upon the gate she saw a heavy old-fashioned bell with a rope attached. The fierce wind slashed the raindrops at her bare arms like some instrument of torture. You could have imagined the drops were small jagged stones instead of merely water.

Standing in what looked like a running river of mud, she reached up and held on to the bell-pull. The house, in early days a farmhouse, had been built close to the road on high ground with the reserve stretching beyond it and into the valley below. Surely someone would hear her. It wasn't so late, only prematurely dark because of the storm. She swung the rope again and the clangour of the great bell filled the air with noise that rivalled the muttering thunder and the shriek of the wind, whining along the fence like some demented harpist. She let go and listened, and, a few yards away, she could hear something crashing through the bush, snuffles, grunts, then a weird screeching and cackling as if a witch were taking off on her broomstick to ride into the teeth of the storm.

'Oh, dear God!' she murmured, and the exclamation was a prayer for help. Perry clutched at the rope end and this time went on ringing until her arm felt it might break off with the effort.

Again there came that awful screeching and this time it seemed even nearer. She gave another despairing tug and held on to the wet rusty metal as if her life depended upon it, the noise of the storm and of the bell mixed up in her tired mind like a nightmare.

'What on earth's going on here?'

She heard a voice now, and it was the voice that had so often penetrated in to her sleep, but now it was real and the gates that had remained barred in her dreams were opening now, the chain rattling as it was released, and hands that she had thought never to feel again upon her were holding her as she fell against him. By the headlights of the car, she could see him now, chestnut hair wetted to black by the rain, golden eyes darkened by night, but the same Tarquin, and, as he held her, she was aware of the hardness of his chest muscles against the clinging wetness of her shirt. She drew away from him and he dropped his hands from her as she stood swaying weakly in the rainswept night.

'Good lord, girl, what are you doing travelling here alone in the wilderness on such a night and in the middle of a storm? It's no kind of weather for a dog to be out, much less a woman on her own!'

He hadn't recognised her, but how could he be expected to? It was dark and he hadn't met her for five years. But surely when she spoke? She had to shout above the noise of the tempest.

'I was coming here to Lion's Rock to see you when I was overtaken by the storm. I should have got here earlier, but I was delayed.'

She saw him shake his head.

'You came hoping to stay here? What a pity you didn't think to make enquiries first. We no longer cater for visitors in the Reserve. We haven't done so for—let's see, about five years. All the huts are closed up now. I'm not very partial to tourists these days.'

Perry wondered what he expected her to do now. Did he think she could get back into the car and drive off into the storm?

'I didn't really come for a holiday!' she shouted.

'No? Well, whatever you came for we'd better get you under shelter. You can explain your visit later. At the moment we both need to dry out.'

She looked up at him and at that moment lightning tore the sky. She could see his hair plastered in sculptured curls across his brow, and she could feel the raindrops running down her own face like tears. But there was no sign of recognition in those eyes that had been so instantly known to her.

'We'd better get you inside before you catch pneumonia.'

He started to guide her back to the car and she felt ice-cold water splashing around her ankles.

'Are you fit to drive?' he asked. 'It's only about a hundred yards from here but lions rather like this area between here and the house.'

The seat of the small car groaned as he got in beside her and she was vividly aware of the warmth of his heavy thigh against the tight wet fabric of her slacks. The spray of water was window-high as the car lurched over the muddy road. Why hadn't he recognised her voice? She could have picked his out from the recordings of a hundred male voices. There had never been anyone else in her life with quite that kind of deep virile tone. But he wasn't expecting her. When they arrived at the house and he saw her in the full light, he was certainly in for a surprise.

Another gate and another fence, then a tree-lined driveway leading to the beautiful homestead, the house she had known so well. When last she saw this avenue of jacaranda trees, it had been heavy with purple blooms and the fallen petals had lain upon the ground as if the trees were reflected in some still pool. The sound of summer had been caught in the murmurings of the bees among the trusses of bell-like flowers. But now the branches were whipped by the fierce wind into streaming black witch's hair and the broad flight of steps up to the wide columned verandah was swept by a dangerous deluge of water.

'Leave the car,' Tarquin shouted. 'I'll see to it later. Get into the house.'

Perry stumbled as her drenched shoes met the smooth wet surface of the steps and she felt his arm go around her, grasping her tightly and propelling her upwards at a breakneck pace. Breathless, feeling half drowned, she was thrust, dripping, into the hallway. It was just as it had been before, the glossy terra-cotta floor, the glowing Persian rugs, the gleaming copper, the lion skin in front of the hearth and the horns of the immense kudu bull at the turn of the stairs.

His hand, that had felt as if it might break her ribs, loosened its hold, but he grasped her shoulders now and turned her face to the light.

'Let's have a look at you. I'm curious to know what kind of mermaid has been washed up on my doorstep.'

The light of the lamp was full on her now and she felt herself trembling, her heart beating wildly. Now the moment she had so long dreaded had arrived. She expected astonishment from him, and, although she was chilled to the bone, her cheeks were burning now from the desperate embarrassment of this meeting. But it had to be faced.

She lifted her head and looked straight into those eyes that had always seemed so strange to her with their tawny

golden gaze. They were like the eyes of some fierce wild
creature, proud and unpredictable, but now, as he stood
there, they seemed as well to have the blank indifference
she had seen once in the eyes of a lion sitting regally under
a tree in the wilderness while his mate rolled submissively
beside him. This cold arrogance affected her with a kind of
anger that made her stammer as she spoke.

'Don't look at me like that! I know you must be surprised to see me after all this time, but I had to come.
There was no other way. I know you never wanted to meet
me again, but once we have talked together I'll go away
again.'

The aloof indifference was replaced by a puzzled frown.
Perry had forgotten how vividly she had memorised each
feature, those thick slanting brows, that quivered now over
the black fringed gold of his eyes.

'Who are you?' Tarquin demanded. 'Should I know
you?'

It was as if she had stepped into a lift shaft where she
had expected solid ground.

'You don't recognise me? My name is Perry Vaughan.'

He shook his head.

'Sorry, I'm afraid not. Have you stayed here before. So
many people came to stay in the old days. It was hard to
keep track of all of them.'

'But, Tarquin,' she said desperately, 'you must remember me. I stayed here five years ago. We knew each
other ... we knew each other very well, perhaps too well,'
she added almost to herself.

How could she tell this man who was regarding her as a
stranger that she had believed herself to be married to
him?

The quizzical dark brows were raised high above those
dangerous golden eyes.

'What was our relationship, then? Are you implying that

there was some kind of attraction between us? I must confess that, when we ran the Reserve as a tourist attraction, I was younger and less wise than I am now. We had very many women visitors and I made the most of it as any man would, but I'm afraid I don't recall your face at all. Can you fill me in on the details?'

I need time to think about this, thought Perry. She was soaked to the skin and after the long journey her tired mind refused to deal with this strange situation. But she made one more effort.

'Actually I didn't stay in the Reserve. I was staying with my grandparents, the Vaughans.'

'Yes, yes, of course. I knew the Vaughans; they were good friends of mine. I was terribly sorry when they died within a few days of each other. But I don't recollect meeting you. You must, however, have been a child then.'

'Seventeen,' Perry informed him. 'Certainly I was very young.'

'I suppose that accounts for it. My tastes ran to more experienced women in those days. And if you were a very young girl I probably made more impression on you than you did on me.'

'It certainly would seem so,' said Perry drily.

He still has a very good opinion of himself, she thought. But how could he have forgotten me completely? Perhaps because he wants to. Or is he pretending?

'However, you haven't explained yet the reason for your visit here. Don't tell me it was just to renew your acquaintance with me?'

He was standing upon the lion rug in front of the hearth and his face seemed to her to have something of the primitive wildness of the beast at his feet.

I'll have to lead up to it, she thought despairingly. I can't tell him now. What can I tell him? She used the first excuse that came into her head.

'I ... I do articles with photographs for magazines and newspapers. I wondered if you would give me permission to do some on the Reserve.'

She felt ashamed of her subterfuge and she started to cough. Icy drips were falling from her hair down her back and she felt herself shivering.

She saw him cross to a thick embroidered bell pull near the hearth and, somewhere in the depths of the great house, she heard a muffled peal.

'I'm not very sold on articles about the Reserve, Miss Vaughan. I don't need publicity. I was persuaded to do a television show some little time ago and I've regretted it ever since. I've had too many foolish females phoning me at all hours in the last weeks. I'm afraid you've made your journey in vain. I think you'd better be on your way to-morrow, but at the moment I'd recommend a hot bath and some supper.'

The opportunity for explanation seemed to be slipping away from her. She must speak now, ask him about the marriage. It was nonsense to think he didn't recognise her. But, just as she was wondering how to start, an African servant in a white uniform with a red fez on his head came softly into the room and stood there bowing, his hands placed in front of him respectfully.

'Oh, Shadrac, take the *nkosizane* to a guest room and see that she has what she needs. Take her some hot soup and some kind of a meal and serve breakfast in her room to-morrow. You can wake her early, because she'll need to leave at first light.'

Tarquin had turned aside and was not even looking in her direction. Feeling utterly defeated, Perry followed Shadrac up the stairs.

She was shown to a room at the end of a long passage far away from the main part of the house. In any other cir-cumstances she might have enjoyed the luxury of her surroundings, the piquant contrast between the strange sounds of the African night outside her window and the spacious room with its soft rose-coloured carpeting and white fur rugs and its wide bed with the cover of muted shades of rose and blue, all bathed in the creamy opalescence of lamp light.

Shadrac had retrieved her small suitcase from the car and now, in the adjoining bathroom, she stripped off her wet clothes and ran a deep hot bath, using the verbena-scented bath essence that she found on a glass shelf. It was a very expensive kind, she noticed. Certainly Tarquin looked after the needs of his presumably rare guests. Perry knew that she must try to work things out, but at the moment all she needed was physical comfort. She lay for a long time in the bath, her long, lovely legs floating in the silky green water, but although now her body was warm and at ease, her brain seemed to remain numb.

When she came back into the room, she found that a tray had been left on the table and, lifting the lids, she discovered hot soup smelling deliciously of herbs and some grilled tiger fish with a dish of beautifully cooked straw potatoes and a salad of oranges and avocado pears. Surprisingly she found she could eat, and, when she had finished the whole meal, she placed the tray outside so as not to be disturbed again and went over to the window where a door led on to a small verandah high above the surrounding trees.

The rain had stopped now and a large golden moon was trying to dismiss the hurrying clouds. From the darkness on all sides came the deafening clamour of frogs, cicadas and crickets, interrupted now and again by the squabbling of monkeys and the keening sound of a jackal yelping at the moon. The forest breathed out its fragrance of wild jasmine mingled with other more acrid herbal scents and, somewhere from the direction of the servants' quarters, came the pungent smell of woodsmoke.

The sounds and scents brought home to Perry, as nothing else could, the fact that she was back in Africa and some eight thousand miles from her settled, ordered life. What was she doing here? She felt now that she had made a bad mistake in insisting that she herself must come. She should have left it to Sinclair to get this muddle sorted out as he had suggested. She had blundered badly when she had failed to explain to Tarquin the real reason for her presence here—but, considering the circumstances, what could she have done? In her exhausted state, she had felt unable to give the true explanation. But the puzzling thing was that he had denied completely that he had ever met her. Was it possible that the whole affair could have meant so little to him that now he did not even know who she was?

She closed the door upon the strange clamour of the tropical night and came back into the room, and, as she brushed out the shining curtain of her hair, dry now and like palest silk in the lamp light, she resolved that she must wake early and try to see Tarquin tomorrow to explain. Slipping between the cool sheets, she vowed to herself that next day she would confront him with the facts. And what were the facts? She turned the lamp down, but in the darkness the sounds of the wild outdoors persisted and that past she had for so long tried to ignore came rushing back to her. It was like one of those African rivers, dry for months, then suddenly tempestuously coming down in flood. Scenes flickered disjointedly across her tired mind. Meeting Tarquin for the first time—she remembered it still. He was standing on the verandah of her grandfather's house, in his hand a glass of beer that was turned to glowing topaz by the strong sunlight flashing through the crimson bougainvillaea flowers festooning the pillars. His open safari jacket revealed the strong column of his neck above the bronzed chest, his face, evenly tanned had a squarish jaw and high cheekbones, and as she caught his glance she had been surprised by the strange beauty of his eyes, brown-gold with a hint of emerald. She was conscious of those eyes, golden animal eyes, scrutinising her appearance, and all at once she had been shakingly aware of herself, conscious of her long slim legs in ridiculously brief shorts and the blue shirt that clung to her small high breasts.

'Well,' said Tarquin, 'I didn't realise your granddaughter was so adult. I expected a child.'

'She is a child,' Grandma protested. 'A very dear child. Young people grow up far too soon these days.'

He doesn't think I'm a child, thought Perry, and a great thrill, half joy, half fear, swept over her.

Lying now in her wide bed, she thought, how did it happen? How could I have become so infatuated with him so quickly? But I was so young, and I'd never met anyone half as much a man as Tarquin.

Another scene flashed before her: their first kiss on the verandah in the darkness when he had come to dinner and they had been left alone there.

'I never could resist temptation,' he had murmured, and his mouth had come down upon hers, hard and strong while her own was soft and yielding, and ever after that she had longed for his touch with a desire that was strange to her and utterly intoxicating.

And she had suffered jealousy too for the first time. Lorraine, she remembered, that was her name. Married to another game ranger, Darrell, but startlingly intimate with Tarquin. She recalled a shining waterfall of black hair, melting dark eyes and a creamy perfect skin, hands exquisitely manicured and adorned with rings, those hands that touched him possessively whenever they talked together.

But she had forgotten about Lorraine when she had been left alone in the wilderness with Tarquin. I was in a dream, she thought, and in that dream nothing existed but the two people who were dreaming it. Almost asleep now, she began to recall the tender sensual charm of those few days in the wilderness, but a shutter seemed to slide down over those last hours.

I'll think about it another time, she thought. Now all I want to do is sleep.

But as the curtains seemed to draw together over those scenes from the past, she found herself asking, Did I ever awake from that dream?

CHAPTER TWO

IN the tree near her window there was a coucal, its bubbling call mingling with the murmur of the wind in the branches. From that other time Perry remembered the sound of its notes, liquid as falling water, a large shy bird, flashing red-brown, white and grey. As she woke to the lovely sound, for a few moments she knew perfect happiness, utter peace that at last she was back where she belonged, and then it all came rushing back to her, the memories of the past and the shattering disillusion of the previous night. She must rouse herself now and try to find the strength of will to face the inevitable scene with Tarquin.

But she didn't want to. All she wanted at this moment was to lie here basking in the warmth and comfort of this soft bed, seeing the sunshine dappling the rosy carpet with the reflection of leaves, and hearing the calls of exotic birds. From this dreamy state, she was suddenly aroused to full consciousness by an abrupt tattoo on the door. This would be the servant with her breakfast. She remembered how Tarquin had ordered that it should be brought to her. Calling a sleepy 'Come in', she sat up in bed and drew her gown towards her. But it was Tarquin who came striding into the room, carrying a mug of coffee which he thrust into her hands.

'Drink this quickly and get dressed. You must be on your way without any delay. I've had a phone call from higher up country to warn us that the river is coming down in

25

flood. If you don't get going straight away, God knows when you'll be able to get across the causeway again.'

He was looking at her now as she sat up in bed, her blonde hair touching her bare shoulders, where the filmy lawn nightgown was held by tiny straps and the lacy frill half concealed, half revealed her creamy breasts. She remembered in a flashing instant how he had gazed and gazed at her during the few rapturous intimate days of their marriage, and yet there was not the slightest sign of recognition in that cool expression.

'But ... but won't the roads be dangerous now?'

'Not very. Once you get to the main road, it will be perfectly safe. I'll escort you as far as the causeway. I assure you I wouldn't push any woman into real danger, but while there's still time you'd better make a run for it. There's no room in my kind of life for women, and I've no desire to have a strange one on my hands for days on end.'

'And I have no desire to stay here with you,' Perry was stung to reply. 'But I came to ask you something and, when I've done so, I assure you nothing will give me greater pleasure than to go.'

'Miss Vaughan, believe me, we really have no time for discussion now, and I told you last night I don't need publicity. I thought you understood that that was my final word on the subject. Just get dressed now, there's a good girl. I'll start the car for you and get one of the Africans to bring a truck along to get me back. Don't take too long to dress. There's no time to lose.'

And then he was gone. Perry, fuming, did as she was told, flinging the few things she had unpacked back into her suitcase. What now? She was puzzled. Did he really not know her or was he just pretending and this was a good excuse to get rid of her? As she ran down the stairs, she heard him sounding the hooter impatiently.

The road was still muddy in spite of the fact that now

the sun was shining, and she did not refuse when Tarquin offered to take the wheel as far as the causeway. He drove faster than she would have done in the circumstances, sliding and skidding over the rough road. Perry's mind was in a turmoil. In this situation she felt as if she were being thrust further and further away from her objective. The strong fierce stranger who was hurtling herself and her car away from Lion's Rock was not the man she had so adored in that sunlit past, and how could she prevent his determination to get rid of her as quickly as possible?

'The road seems very difficult,' she managed to say as they slewed around a sharp bend at a breakneck pace.

'Once you get over the causeway, it will straighten out. The Met. people say there's more bad weather to come in the next few days. Far better you should go now while you still can.'

'But what happens to the Reserve when the river comes down?'

'We just sit it out. We keep plenty of supplies in case of emergency. And now we don't have visitors, there's no crisis about getting them back to their homes. We often have to organise a rescue operation for animals stranded on the islands up-river. It's all in the day's work. Now, look, stop talking, and let me concentrate on getting us over this mud. We've no time to lose.'

This certainly was not the time to turn to Tarquin and say, 'Don't you remember that once I was your wife ... at least I thought I was? But was it all pretence? You're the only one who can tell me.'

No, now she would have to go back to Sinclair and admit her failure and ask him to do it his way for now she felt more confused than ever. She glanced secretly at Tarquin's profile, clear-cut against the azure blue sky beyond the car window. Even now the very physical presence of this man she had once known so intimately could have the effect of making her heart turn over. But it was fear, not attraction, she told herself, that made her shiver as she recalled how she had once trembled at the touch of those bronzed hands upon her body.

And now they were nearing the causeway, that narrow long bridge she had scarcely noticed in her journey the day before. Yesterday there had been shallow pools, but now, as they came down the steep approach, the water was foaming around the concrete supports and gradually creeping over the roadway.

'It's under water already, but the flood waters haven't arrived yet. I'll get you across and then walk back. Shadrac is following us with a truck and he'll soon catch up.'

It was now or never, Perry thought. As they halted and he watched the river, she turned to Tarquin saying,

'Look at me. Do you really not remember me?'

She had got his attention now and a strange baffled expression seemed to cross his face.

'You're very persistent, aren't you? But sorry, no, I can't recall that we ever met. Yet you have a very distinctive appearance, those huge blue eyes and the perfect skin. Some men might find you quite beautiful.'

'But you don't?'

'I didn't say that. But, look, whatever you came for, whether the journalism was just an excuse to further our so-called long-ago acquaintance, it's too late now. You may have thought it important, but it isn't of any importance to me. I must get you across the river. That's the priority.'

His words drummed inside her mind as the car edged slowly towards the river and into the shallow water surging over the causeway. They were halfway across when suddenly the engine started to splutter and died on them.

'Damnation, there's water in the engine! I intended to take the fan belt off, but you interrupted me with your foolish questions. Just like a woman to start an irrelevant conversation at the wrong moment!'

'It's not my fault. It's yours for being so keen to get rid of me. What do we do now?'

'Stay in the car, but get into the driver's seat and I'll get out and try to give it a push. Shadrac should be here soon and he'll be able to help.'

With the car engine silenced, Perry could hear all kinds of noises, the swish of the wind in the trees, the sound of the swiftly running river, but now she was aware of another sound, like far-off thunder, and yet there was not a cloud in the sky.

'What's that noise?' she asked Tarquin just as she was stepping out of the car. 'Is it another storm coming?'

He paused, listening, as if what she said was just another exasperating delay, and then his expression changed.

'It's the river. We're too late—it's coming down. We'll have to run for it. There's no time to lose.'

Perry seized her handbag and camera equipment while he muttered at the delay and then he was pulling her out of the car and dragging her across the flooded causeway. The water was deeper now and she felt it lapping thigh high against her legs, pushing her backwards as she tried to lift her limbs and force her way through the swirling current.

'Can't you move any faster?' she heard him shout impatiently.

'No, I can't. You're killing me as it is!'

'For heaven's sake, girl, get a move on! Do you want us both to drown?'

The waves lapped higher and if it had not been for his fierce grasp around her waist she would have been swept away by the strong current. They reached the bank and still he would not let her pause for breath although she felt as if her lungs were being pierced with red-hot irons, but he pushed her up the steep bank until she was high above the river. They were only just in time. As they reached the higher ground, a great wall of dark brown water swept along the already flooded river and foaming yellow angry waves overwhelmed the little car, pushing it off the causeway and down the stream.

'But the car, oh, the car!' sobbed Perry, feeling cold and numb with shock.

She was not sure whether Tarquin's hand around her shoulders was meant to strengthen or to shake her.

'You're safe, aren't you?' he demanded. 'Good grief, woman, be sensible, and for heaven's sake, stop that. I never could stand seeing a woman weep.'

She remembered he had said that all those years ago the day they had parted, and the shock of hearing the same words again in such a different context made her pull herself together.

'It's unfortunate about the car, but it's hired, isn't it, so it will be insured against accident. We'll phone them when we get back to the house. It seems I'm to have your company for a while longer than we expected.'

He didn't sound as if he liked the idea, thought Perry.

'Ah, there's Shadrac, come just too late to be of any help.'

He was of some help, thought Perry, as they drove back to the house. With Shadrac there she had to repress the seething indignation she felt at the way Tarquin had reacted to the fact that she would have to stay longer. Did he think she wanted to stay? After the way he had spoken to her this morning, all she wanted now was to get as far away from him as possible. Oh, why hadn't she left it all to Sinclair to sort out?

Back at the house, Shadrac without waiting to be asked went off in the direction of the kitchen to make coffee. Left alone with Tarquin, Perry found she had nothing to say. The rapid events of the morning had temporarily banished any idea of telling him the real reason for her visit.

She had wanted more time and now it seemed she had got it. Now all that remained was to choose the right moment. And this wasn't it, she thought, as she regarded her reluctant host's expression as he thrust a mug of hot coffee into her hand.

'Sit down and drink this,' he told her. 'I'll phone the Met. people as soon as we've had this and we'll find out what the prospects are. The scene may have changed since this morning. Let's hope so anyway.'

He did not seem to wish to talk, so she sat in silence, terribly conscious of his presence and yet hardly daring to look at him. They were sitting on the verandah, for they were both mud-bespattered and yet he had insisted that she should drink her coffee before going to wash. In the thick pottery mugs it was scalding hot.

'Drink it down and stop shivering, girl,' Tarquin said.

He was looking at her now and at last seemed to take in her exhausted, bedraggled appearance.

'Have you anything to change into?'

She had held on to her handbag when they left the car, but all it contained was money, her papers and cosmetics.

'No, of course I haven't. All the clothes I had with me have gone down the river with the car.'

'Too bad, but you must realise this part of Africa is a savage place. Or didn't you know that? I thought I made it clear enough in that television show.'

'I didn't even see it,' cried Perry, feeling exasperated. 'You're not so famous that your films appear in London.'

'London? Are you from the U.K.? Well, that would account for your ignorance of local conditions. The river coming down is only one of the dangers we face here. It's nothing unusual really. It happens all of six times a year around these parts.'

Before she could reply, he had gone and she heard him picking up the phone somewhere in the house. His deep voice was clearly audible in the noonday hush of this wilderness area and she remained still, listening to his side of the conversation.

'Yes, yes, I know the river has come down, I was in it. No, nothing much. No harm done. More bad weather on the way? Hell, how long are you expecting it to last? I see. That's bad. No, no, we have enough supplies. Nothing like that. It's just that there's a tourist here who should have left today. Helicopters all grounded? Well, she'll just have to wait. Too bad. So long.'

She heard him slam down the phone, then straight away pick it up again. His voice sounded softer this time and she had some difficulty in hearing what he was saying, but she listened unashamedly. If she had to stay here, she was determined to know what was going on.

'Hello, my dear,' she heard, and then only snatches of the conversation. 'About the same size. Just slacks and T-shirts will do. No, you don't know her. A young woman named Perry Vaughan. She says she visited here some years ago. That would have been in your time, wouldn't it? No, I can't say I remember her, though she seems to think I should.'

So it was true. He really didn't know her, for why should he pretend to someone else? But who was he phoning? He seemed to be borrowing some clothes for her. Could it be his girl-friend? When he came back he seemed in a better mood. Her heart jolted as she recognised the charm of his smile so long forgotten.

'Bad news for you, I'm afraid. They expect this kind of weather to continue and the river to remain impassible possibly for another week. You'll have to stay here. There isn't a helicopter available—you may be sure I asked about that. However, I phoned a friend and she's bringing some clothes for you to wear. It's fortunate you seem to be about the same size, medium height and slender. Women are a bit thin on the ground around here, but this one is married to a game ranger down the road.'

So it wasn't his girl-friend as Perry had feared, for what could she have done if she had found that Tarquin was engaged or even if he had been already married to someone else? Kept quiet? But that would not have solved her difficulty. No, somehow she must find out the truth of that long-ago ceremony in the African village.

'Meanwhile I can provide you with a towelling robe. It will be rather large, but you can come down to lunch in it.'

So now she was to be allowed to eat with him and not banished to her own room. She washed away the river mud with hot water and then indulged in a cooling shower, and by the time she had finished, Shadrac had left a dark blue robe on her bed, taking away with him the muddy slacks, the jacket and her underwear. She had used the lemon verbena cologne and talc and was glad to be fragrant and clean again instead of having that awful dank river smell in her nostrils, and now she wrapped herself in the blue robe, tying it tightly around her waist but rather dismayed at the idea of lunching with Tarquin clad only in this one garment. She twisted her damp hair high on her head, used a pink lipstick and then gazed rather ruefully at her reflection in the long mirror, at the slender bare feet and slim ankles, the pleated folds of material falling from the tightly belted waist.

The large lapels presented her with a problem, for, however much she wrapped them over each other, they tended to fall apart and give the appearance of a deeply plunging neckline. She began to wish that Tarquin had ordered that she should have lunch sent up to her room.

There was a conservatory off the more formal dining room with white wrought-iron furniture, a glass-topped table with delicate lacelike chairs, and a couch of intricately woven cane with deep cushions of orange and white. All around bloomed large tubs of flowering azaleas and other more tropical plants and overhead along the glass roof climbed a jade vine, its bright green flowers hanging down like exquisite pendant lamps. Tarquin was already there, glass in hand, looking as immaculate in his clean safari suit as if the flooded river had never existed.

'Shadrac has left our meal ready and we'll help ourselves. I thought it best he go to organise some help with the laundry. You'll be glad of your own clothes as soon as possible, I suppose, though I must say that robe looks much more attractive on you than it does on me.'

Perry clutched the errant lapels tightly together and wished she had had the sense to ask Shadrac for a safety pin.

'And there's absolutely no need to look like an embarrassed spinster, because I'm quite sure you are not. Any girl who brings herself to Africa under her own steam and comes to visit a man who lives alone in the wilderness can't be exactly a shrinking violet, isn't that so? It's entirely your own fault that you find yourself stuck here, so you'd better decide to make the best of it.'

'In what way?' asked Perry.

His hard eyes mocked her. How, she asked herself, even at seventeen, could she ever have thought herself in love with this man?

'I gather that we're supposed to have had some relationship in the past, according to you. If you're hoping to resume this fictional romance, I'd advise you to forget it. I'm averse to women who try to take advantage of a seemingly promising situation.'

'Promising? You must be joking!'

Perry tried to look haughty, but felt this was difficult dressed as she was in an inadequate bathrobe. 'Mr Winslow, I wish you would lose this idea that I came here because of your irresistible charm. I don't see anything promising about being stuck in the wilderness for possibly days on end with a man who's been insufferably rude to me since the moment he set eyes on me.'

'I've been perfectly civil to you, more than civil in fact. And if we're to be together for some time you'd better drop this "Mr Winslow". My name is Tarquin. And whose fault is it that you're here anyway? Certainly not mine. Now come along. Have a glass of sherry and let me enjoy my beer in peace. If you're to stay here, you'd better learn to tolerate the situation. I suppose you're used to men who listen to every word and do whatever you wish.'

'I'm used to men who are civilised,' said Perry.

She accepted a glass of sherry and sat sipping it and watching a malachite sunbird sipping honey from a flower just outside the window, but she was hardly seeing the green beauty of its iridescent plumage. Instead she was wondering, what has happened to him? Even allowing for the illusions of a seventeen-year-old girl, this man is not like the one I thought I married all that time ago. There's something odd here. Did I only see the best side of his character then? Possibly. He was strong-willed and a bit frightening even then, but surely he was not of such an intractable disposition as he seems to be now.

It becomes more and more impossible to tell him why I came here. It would make an awkward situation a hundred times worse. If I were able to go immediately I had asked him, and this is how I intended it should be, it wouldn't be so bad, but now I'm stuck here, how can I do it? But I don't understand. How can he have forgotten me entirely? I haven't forgotten him. Every gesture he makes brings back memories of that time. And yet it meant nothing to him.

'Is there anyone who'll be missing you, anyone you should get in touch with?' asked Tarquin. 'The telephone is still working and you may use it if you wish, of course.'

Should she phone Sinclair? But what could she tell him? Better leave it and await developments. Sinclair liked everything to be clear-cut. She would hardly be able to convey to him over this long distance just how impossible her situation had become.

'There's no one to miss me, and my return flight is not booked yet.'

'You surprise me. I should have thought a woman as beautiful as you would have half a dozen men around, or at least one who would be anxious to know her whereabouts.'

'The one who matters most knows where I am.'

'So I was right—there is a special one. And what was he doing to let you come all this way on your own?'

'Certainly as things have turned out now I wish I hadn't,' Perry retorted.

'Well, cheer up, while you're here you may be able to see something of the reserve if the weather clears. And you can get photographs. They should be publishable so long as you don't name this particular place. I don't particularly object to that if it's done properly and strictly under my supervision. What I won't tolerate is a personal interview, so don't you dare to do a profile of me for a magazine just on the strength of our small acquaintance.'

The iced papaya sprinkled with lemon juice and then the cold partridge with some exotic salad was delicious. Why, thought Perry, could she not be left to enjoy it without having to be riled by Tarquin's overbearing manner?

'I didn't come here with any idea of writing a personal profile about you. What gave you that idea?'

'Only that since I did that television show I've been deluged with requests for personal interviews from women who write for magazines. And you seem to be another of them. Isn't that why you tried to claim some previous acquaintance with me?'

'No, it's not,' said Perry.

She felt goaded now almost to the point of telling him the real reason for her arrival here, whatever the consequences.

'I find that hard to believe. So many women have come here vowing that they didn't intend to write anything personal about me, only articles about the animals, and then the next thing there's been some ghastly claptrap about the romantic figure I cut as a game ranger in some cheap women's magazine. Perhaps too you're one of the women who think a game ranger would be exciting for a quick affair? I've met plenty of those kind.'

Perry sprang up from the table. Now she had really had enough!

'You really are the most insufferably conceited man I've ever met! You seem to have a highly inflated idea of your own devastating charm, but I can assure you I'm not one of those women journalists bowled over by your television appearance.'

The golden eyes seemed to be assessing her coolly.

'No? So why did you come?'

'If you really want to know, I'll tell you.'

They had both risen now and were facing each other like two angry cats. Suddenly he strode across and seized her by the shoulders. The gown had slipped aside and she was conscious of his large strong hands bruising the firm curves of her upper arms. He was laughing and for a moment she seemed to be back in that other time when his laughter had meant love to her. But now she recognised the quality of mockery in it, and, even as she remembered the thrilling sensation of those hands upon her body, she knew that now he was making game of her.

'Why, Perry, you look quite magnificent when you're angry, like one of those avenging furies or a Valkyrie— with those golden locks rampant as a lion's mane and those breasts thrust forward in the revealing gown, you could be a model for a figurehead of an old sailing ship. Only no figurehead ever had such huge flashing sapphire eyes. But go on, I've interrupted you, yet I'm all ears to know why you came here. If it wasn't for an interview and not for the sake of my manly charm, what was it for?'

He was still holding her, his face very close to hers. She could see the small emerald flecks in those strange golden eyes and each black curling spike of those lashes that were so long for a man's, and she felt on her own skin the rough dark tendrils of hair springing from his bronzed chest, and knew the poignancy of that remembered fragrance, virile, aromatic, the essence of Tarquin.

'Am I interrupting something?'

Tarquin dropped his hands as if he had been touching a flame, and Perry stood swaying on her feet, trying to gather the loose folds of her robe about her, utterly dismayed. Lorraine! Of course it must be she whom Tarquin had meant when he spoke of a ranger's wife who had recently returned to live here. It was she whom Tarquin had asked for the loan of slacks and shirts. Perry would have known her anywhere. Her dark attraction was unchanged, and yet she was looking at Perry as if she had never seen her before. But of course she had come upon them in what looked like a rather intimate pose. Perhaps she was embarrassed and this had brought the look of blank distaste upon that lovely face.

'Shadrac didn't answer the door and you two seemed to be otherwise engaged. Introduce me, Tarquin.'

There was a cool insolence in the way she stared at Perry, but no apparent recognition.

'Surely we met some years ago,' Perry said hesitantly.

Could she herself have changed so much? she asked herself wildly. Why did no one know her? But of course she had met Lorraine infrequently and it had been because she felt so jealous that it had meant so much more to her than it had to Lorraine.

'I don't think so,' Lorraine answered sharply. 'You must be thinking of someone else.'

But even as she denied it, Perry was seized with a very strong conviction that the other girl was lying. With Tarquin it had been different. She was sure now that he had no recollection of her whatsoever, puzzling as that might be. But Lorraine knew her, remembered her from that previous visit, but for some reason was not going to admit it. There was a falseness about her denial that made Perry believe it was a pretence. Perry made up her mind that she must see Lorraine alone and tax her with this. Why should she, Perry, appear to be totally unknown to both Tarquin and Lorraine?

'Perry says she visited here some five years ago in the days when we still had tourists around,' said Tarquin. 'That would have been at about the same time that you were here, before Darrell transferred to the National Park. She appears to remember us more clearly than we remember her. Of course we had hundreds of visitors in those days, so it's little wonder we don't recall it.'

'Yes, there were other things occupying our minds at that time,' said Lorraine in what Perry though was a meaningful way.

'Lorraine's husband, Darrell, left here to take up some important work in a bigger Government Reserve, but has had to come back here to lighter work because he caught malaria,' Tarquin explained.

'Tarquin has been enormously kind to us and has let us live in a lovely farmhouse he acquired recently.'

But that must be her grandparents' old farm, Perry thought. However, she did not say anything. It was all confusing enough without bringing that up.

'I've brought jeans and shirts in a suitcase. Would you

like to come upstairs and try them?' asked Lorraine, casting a critical look at Perry's figure.

'You might find them a bit tight. You aren't quite as slim as me, are you?'

'Shadrac has brought his wife in to wash Perry's own clothes,' Tarquin said. 'She'll just need the odd change of garment. We'll hope the river goes down soon.'

'I hope so too for your sake, Tarquin,' said Lorraine. 'I always find that unexpected guests are such a bind, don't you?'

Everyone around here seems to go in for plain speaking, Perry thought, but she followed Lorraine up to the bedroom where the other girl had instructed a servant to take the suitcase.

'They're a bit washed out, I'm afraid,' Lorraine told Perry, producing some faded denim jeans and old T-shirts from the case. 'Actually I'd put these aside for an African jumble sale, but I thought you wouldn't mind wearing them if you were desperate.'

'It's very kind of you to lend them to me,' Perry told her a little insincerely.

The clothes Lorraine had brought for her were certainly not very becoming and she thought with regret of her own few elegant garments lost with the car down river. As she changed into the tight blue denim jeans and faded pink Indian shirt, she was conscious of Lorraine's curious gaze and she was quite sure that the other woman knew who she was in spite of her denial.

'It's strange that neither you nor Tarquin remember anything about my previous visit,' she ventured to say at last.

Lorraine's dark eyes flickered away from her careful examination of Perry's appearance.

'Why should you think it strange? We had hundreds of visitors when the reserve was open to tourists. As Tarquin said, we couldn't possibly remember them all. And I didn't even come in contact with the holiday people, so how could I have met you?'

'I was not a tourist in the Reserve. I stayed with my grandparents on their farm for quite a long while. I remember you were a dinner guest in this house at the same time as we were.'

Lorraine shook her head blankly.

'Sorry, I have no recollection of it.'

'It seems impossible that Tarquin shouldn't remember me,' persisted Perry.

'For heaven's sake, why? Tarquin must have met dozens of girls in those days and they all flung themselves at him. He used to enjoy it. But nowadays I must say he's much more discriminating.'

So now I know where I stand, thought Perry. I was just one of the girls who flung themselves at Tarquin.

'I think I should warn you, if you're going to stay here for a while, that he's not to be trusted with women even now. I hope you haven't come here with any bright ideas about the dashing Tarquin Winslow. He's a bit disillusioned with women since he did that T.V. show and they all started heading this way, falling over themselves to seduce him, but he still makes the most of his opportunities when an attractive girl hands herself to him on a plate as you seemed to be doing when I broke up the happy scene.'

'I think I can look after myself as far as Tarquin is concerned. Don't worry, he doesn't attract me in the least.'

And that's true, Perry vowed to herself. He's no longer the man I thought I loved better than my life.

'Why should I worry?' asked Lorraine.

Why indeed? With her golden glowing tan, the dark loveliness set off by the amber silk shirt and exotically patterned wrapover skirt, Lorraine need not fear any other woman's attractions. Had she too been in love with Tarquin five years ago? And what was the position now she had come back?

CHAPTER THREE

'I'M afraid you must eat alone this evening. There's more bad weather on the way and I'll have to consult with Darrell and prepare for any emergency,' Tarquin informed Perry when he made a brief appearance at the house after being out during the afternoon. He had gone off to Lorraine's house and left Perry to her own devices and her own dark thoughts.

The only bright spot at the moment was that the car had been hauled out from its place down river. It had come to rest on a narrow sandbank and could possibly be repaired when it had been dried out. Perry had heard Tarquin high-handedly dealing with the hire firm from whom she had borrowed it, and for once was glad of his arrogant manner. She herself could not have coped with the situation half so brazenly, she knew. Her suitcase had been retrieved none the worse for its trip down the river and she was glad to have her own clothes back again and be able to return Lorraine's washed-out slacks and shirts.

All that afternoon the thunder rolled and great storms towered like high buildings in the sky. Later as she prepared for bed after a solitary meal, another storm broke, louder and more violent than that of last night. Where was Tarquin now? she wondered as she lay in bed, listening to the beat of the tropical downpour upon the roof, and the sound of water pouring out in cataracts from the overloaded gutters. Was he out in the storm, or had the bad weather merely served as an excuse to dispense with her company and go to Lorraine's home? Was there some understanding between Tarquin and Lorraine, as there seemed to have been in the past? Perry felt frustrated by her lack of knowledge. What had occurred during these five long years to make Tarquin so different from the man she remembered?

But was he so different? Or at seventeen had she thought him so perfect that she had not noticed any faults? Certainly she had been blinded by his physical attraction. Now, lying sleepless with the sound of the rain like scattered rice falling against the window pane, she remembered those last days. How had it come to that ceremony at the tiny church? Was it that by then, after their days alone together in the wilderness, they seemed to have left the real world and have entered some enchanted dream?

Some days earlier the others in the party had had to return, but she and Tarquin had gone on together and then they had reached a small settlement on the edge of the Reserve, a few African huts perched high above the river where they could get the first rays of the morning sun, and below were wide sandbanks where hippos wallowed and wild banana trees rustled their wide green leaves. The African minister who was in charge showed them into a round thatched hut with adobe floor swept scrupulously clean and quite empty except for two wooden stools and some rolled up mats made of woven grass.

They dined on wild pig, roasted over the coals, the crackling skin delicious and golden brown, and plantains baked in their skins. Tarquin drank the pungent foaming drink that was passed around from hand to hand, the homemade beer that needed a strong head. Maybe it was that which had the relaxing effect, but as later they sat in front of the hut on the grass, his face seemed to have lost that stern expression that had so often made her feel doubtful and afraid.

A moon was rising, huge and golden above the river, and far below they could see three elephants, their dark bulk like polished pewter as they returned from their evening bathe. Tarquin reached over and took Perry's hand. Her heart seemed to leap into her throat as he smoothed her arm saying, 'Have you liked the wilderness trail, Perry?'

'So much,' she whispered shakily. 'Have you?'

'On the whole, yes, though I think I told you before, I'm not a man for resisting temptation. Don't you think I've been remarkably well behaved on this trip, Perry?'

'I suppose so,' she said.

It was such an exquisite feeling, she thought, just to be with Tarquin and to feel that strong brown hand upon her own smooth skin. Now it was tracing the outlines of her face, and the curve of her chin, sweeping back the heavy silk of her haid until it found the sensitive place behind the ears. And all the time she sat submissively, not daring to move in case she frightened this gentle, thrilling hand away.

His face was in her hair now and his hand was at her waist where the clinging shirt left bare the skin above the dark blue jeans, and now she turned her face up to his and they were kissing, deep hungry kisses that seemed to be trying to make up for all those days in the wilderness when they had hardly touched each other's hands. After a while he had lifted her in his strong arms and carried her into the hut where the woven grass mats were fragrant with the scent of Africa, but there he had released her warm clinging arms from about his body.

'This won't do, my innocent Perry. You can't even realise how deeply I desire you. I hate to leave you now, but I must. Tomorrow we'll ask the priest to marry us. What do you say to that?'

And so it had happened, this strange marriage in a little

thatched chapel, herself in her blue shirt and jeans and Tarquin in his khaki safari ranger's uniform, while the smiling African priest intoned the words of the marriage service as solemnly as if he had been a high dignitary of the church, and the children of the village sang a hymn in their own language, sweet and shrill as the bridal couple left the church.

Oh, she had known happiness then, heavenly bliss that had so soon passed and had never come into her life again. Those nights of ecstasy, those days of lovely lassitude had brought her joy that she little knew she was to lose so soon. And then the day had arrived when Tarquin said they must return.

Perry was lying under a flat-topped thorn tree on a hammock swinging gently in the slight breeze from the river with Tarquin sitting beside her, his hand in hers. Below them on the river bank, a herd of elephants jostled each other, the young calves playfully paddling in the shallow water, and the call of an oriole fell like a sigh across the wilderness that was shimmering in the heat of noonday.

'Perry, my dear, we must discuss what's to happen when we return to civilisation.'

'Must we, Tarquin?'

She didn't want to think about it. She only wanted to go on in this blissful dream, not to be brought back to earth.

'I suppose you realise that the only thing to do is to keep this marriage secret,' said Tarquin. 'The old priest won't say anything. He's given his word.'

She was startled. She knew, of course, that it would be a shock to her grandparents, but they liked Tarquin and, if they had to go back to civilisation, as he had called it, she looked forward to being recognised as Tarquin's wife.

'But why, Tarquin? And how can we keep it secret?'

'Quite easily. We must go on as we were before. You must return to stay with your grandparents until I can arrange a formal marriage that will satisfy your family.'

'You mean that we have to separate, that we can't live together when we get back? Oh, no, Tarquin!'

'It won't be for long, believe me, Perry. I'm not going to enjoy the separation any more than you, but if we tell people too soon, I might lose you. We'll be able to meet, of course. You can come over to my house.'

'But that way I'll feel like your mistress, not your wife!'

Now she had angered him, and her spirit quailed at the expression of those golden green eyes.

'I didn't think you were capable of saying such a thing. Be reasonable, Perry. If we go back and announce that we were married by an African priest in the wilderness, there'll be hell to pay.'

'Then why did you do it?' Perry demanded.

'You know damn well why I did it, why we both did it— because we wanted each other and were too impatient to wait.'

Why hadn't he just said, 'Because I love you,' she thought.

For his sake she had acquiesced in the plan. They were to separate when they arrived back, and not to tell anyone of their marriage. As soon as possible, Tarquin was to come and tell the grandparents he wanted to marry Perry. Then there could be a quiet formal ceremony very soon. She had to be content with this, but how could she go back to the pretence of being a young girl, untouched by life, after the thrilling days and nights of joy that she had known?

She had thought that the change in her must surely show, but her grandparents seemed to greet her more vaguely than usual when she returned, and she was soon to find out the reason.

'Thank goodness you're back at last! We hardly expected Tarquin to keep you out on the wilderness trail so long. You must have been enjoying it.'

'Yes, it was fabulous,' said Perry.

'I'm so glad you got on well with Tarquin. He has rather a low opinion of women sometimes and I was a bit worried you might be nervous in his company.'

'No, it was all right,' Perry told her.

All right? Oh, why did she have to deceive them in this way? Why couldn't she tell them her wonderful news?

'Now, Perry darling, I do hope you aren't going to be too disappointed, but we've had word from your aunt that she would like you to come back on the first possible plane. It seems she has to go to hospital for a minor operation.'

'An operation?' asked Perry, alarmed.

'There's no need to be worried. It's nothing very much, but she would like you to come home to look after the house while she's in hospital. I've already phoned about your booking and in fact they can get you on to the plane tomorrow. I just have to confirm it because I wasn't sure you would arrive back in time.'

'But I can't ... how can I?'

'Oh, darling, I knew you'd be disappointed, but it had to end in a few weeks anyway, didn't it?'

Oh, no, it didn't, thought Perry frantically. What am I to do? I can't go home. I must stay here with Tarquin. But he'll know what to do. I've got to see him soon.

She chose a time when her grandparents were out of the way to phone him, though she knew she could not say much because in this part of the world there were party lines and anyone could lift the phone and hear your conversation.

'Tarquin, it's Perry.'

'Why, Perry, I didn't expect to hear from you so soon. I thought we agreed you wouldn't get in touch until you heard from me.'

'I know, Tarquin, but something has come up.'

'What kind of something?'

'You know I can't talk on the phone. When can I see you?'

There was a pause and quite distinctly over the distance she heard a woman's silvery laugh.

'Is someone with you?' she said.

'Lorraine has just arrived.'

'What's she come for?'

His voice sounded exasperated.

'Really, Perry! To welcome me home, I suppose. Look, meet me at that place near the river at seven tomorrow morning. I can't talk now. See you.'

Perry wished she did not feel this terrible flash of jealousy when she thought of Lorraine beside Tarquin. Soon, very soon now, everyone would know that she, Perry, was Tarquin's bride. So why did she feel so desperate and why had she been plunged from the peak of ecstasy to this terrible mood of anxiety? She made a show of packing her clothes and preparing for departure, though she did not really believe it would happen. She had told her grandmother that she wanted to take a last ride over the farm and one of the servants was given instructions to saddle her horse at an early hour. After spending a sleepless night, by half past six she was on her way, the hooves of her horse leaving tracks in the heavy dew.

Doves called to each other in the thickets, their sad amorous song seeming to accord with her own mood. Beaded spiders hung on the spikes of red aloes and starlings flashed cobalt blue in the first rays of the sun. Tarquin was waiting for her, leaning against a tree, his horse tethered beside him, and when she saw him, all her doubts disappeared. When she was in his arms, however, she could not help the quick tears that rained down her face.

'Hold on, what's this? What's wrong, Perry? I can't stand women who cry. I didn't know you were the weeping kind.'

She was hurt by his careless words.

'I'm not usually,' she gasped. 'But, oh, Tarquin, they've booked me to go home today!' And she explained the circumstances. 'What am I to do?'

She had expected him to take her more closely in his arms and assure her that now there was nothing else for it but to confess to their marriage, but he had loosened his hold, and, as she looked up into his face, she saw that his expression was abstracted and grim.

'If she needs you, I suppose you'll have to go,' he muttered.

'But, Tarquin, you can't mean it! How can I leave you now?'

'Of course I don't want you to go. Your aunt isn't the only one who needs you. But for the moment I don't see any way to prevent your going back.'

'But, Tarquin, don't you see, all we have to do is to tell them we're married? Then I can stay. No one can insist on my parting from you.'

She could not believe that he could fail her and that, after all the lovely days they had spent together, he should look at her with this hostile expression as if she were some irritating stranger.

'You must understand, Perry, I can't let people know about us yet. There are too many complications, things to be cleared up before I tell your family I intend to marry you.'

'But we are married!' Perry cried.

'Yes, of course, but I can hardly tell them about that. They'll think, quite rightly, that I took advantage of your youth and innocence.'

'I wanted it too,' she pointed out.

'Yes, my darling, you were lovely. There was no way I could resist you.'

Perry noticed that he was speaking in the past tense. She

felt confused and anxious. She was so inexperienced about men. How could she persuade Tarquin to do something that he was very plainly set against? And what were the complications he spoke of? Could one of them be Lorraine?

He put his arm around her shoulder. She could have wept at this casual gesture, such a contrast to the passionate caresses they had shared in the wilderness. And he spoke to her as if to a child.

'Now, Perry, stop worrying and go back to your home for a while. It will all work out, you'll see. We must go carefully, but as soon as I can manage it, I'll get leave and come to fetch you.'

She turned her tear-stained face to his. What could she do to influence him? She did not even dare to kiss this dark frowning stranger who was really her husband.

'Why won't you tell about our marriage?' she asked. 'Is it because of Lorraine?'

He flinched as if she had struck him.

'Lorraine? What has she to do with it?'

'I thought ... I thought ...'

'Then you thought wrong.'

She noticed that his face underneath the bronze tan had flushed dark red and the gold green eyes flashed fire. She felt quite desperate now. How could she leave him, perhaps for months, when he was feeling angry with her? She put a timid hand to his face that burned with anger.

'Tarquin, I love you so much. Please say you'll come and at least say something to the grandparents before I go. Even if you say I must leave you for a while, I'd like it to be all known to them. I hate all this mystery. Just come and talk to them. We needn't tell anyone else.'

He was silent for so long that she was sure he was going to refuse her. She looked at him and wondered how only yesterday she could have felt she knew him better than herself. She thought of all the lovely intimate things they had shared together. How could it be ending like this? But it wasn't ending. Even if she had to go home for a while, she would be back soon. He would come to fetch her. The whole of their lives stretched in front of them. There was only to be this tiny interruption and then everything would be beautiful again.

He sighed and she thought he sounded exasperated but hoped she was wrong.

'Very well, Perry. I'll come and tell them before you go, though I still think it may be unwise. However, perhaps I owe this to you. But I hardly think it's necessary to tell them about that ceremony in the wilderness—only that I want to marry you now.'

'And you'll come to fetch me from England as soon as you can?'

'Of course. Now go, Perry, before they wonder where you are.'

'Aren't you going to kiss me?' she faltered.

'Not if you're going to start crying again. Now look, Perry, forget it. I'm doing this for the best. You must trust me. Everything will work out.'

'And you don't love Lorraine better than me?'

'That, Perry, is not worth answering.'

Before she could say any more, he had leapt on to his horse and she felt despairingly that he was leaving her in anger.

'You will come to tell them?' she called after him, but he did not reply. She watched the black horse trotting, then galloping, faster and faster over the rough paths until horse and rider were out of sight.

But he would come later to the farm. She was sure of it. He had said he would come to tell her grandparents that he wanted to marry her, and she would have to be satisfied with that. She would have preferred that he should tell them the whole story, but that couldn't be.

All that morning she waited. Her packing was finished and she sat on the swinging seat on the verandah, that place that had been the scene of their first kiss. While her grandmother talked to her, she listened for the sound of the Land Rover's engine or that of a galloping horse, but all she heard was the sound of the mourning doves and the booming call of a ground hornbill, monotonous, insistent, unmusical.

'We'll have an early lunch because you must leave for the airport directly afterwards,' her grandmother told her.

'I have to make a phone call to someone,' she excused herself.

Why had he left it so late? Where could he be? She must know, must speak to him again before she left. She could not go to the airport not even having seen him again. But when she got through to the house, it was a servant who replied, and it was not the African who was in charge of the household but some young one who did not seem able to understand her and could hardly speak English.

'Mr Winslow?' she asked. 'Where is he?'

'Out.'

'But where is he?'

'Gone. Gone to town.'

'To town?'

How could Tarquin have gone to town? Tarquin hated towns and the nearest one was a hundred miles away.

'Are you sure?' she demanded.

But he didn't seem to understand her.

'Where is your master?' she shouted desperately.

'To town. Not good. Gone in with missus.'

'What missus?'

'Boss Darrell's missus.'

Lorraine. He had gone somewhere with Lorraine after promising her he would come to her. How could he have done it? After all these years she remembered how difficult

it had been to hide her shock and dismay from her grandparents, but she knew she could not break down and tell
them the facts now. They naturally put down her sadness
to the fact that she was hating to leave them, hating to
leave Africa, this Africa she had learned to love.

Even then she was hoping there must be some mistake
and that in a few short weeks she would be back, acknow-
ledged as Tarquin's wife. How could she bear it if she
didn't think this was so as the plane rose above the blue
hills of Africa? But she had never returned, never seen this
country again until now. She had written—oh, yes, she had
written to Tarquin, desperate letters spelling out her love.
But he had never replied. For a while she hoped with fear-
ful joy that she might be pregnant. If that had happened,
the smooth lines of her existence would have been swept
away. But it was not to be.

In time the hurt had been hidden behind cool indifference to any suggestion of passion. That was why Sinclair
suited her. He would be content with a wife, mildly affectionate, someone who would take an interest in his career,
who would entertain his business associates in his beautiful
home. Of course that early marriage must have been a
pretence. But she must find out for certain. Yet how could
she when Tarquin had failed to recognise her?

Now, going over that last scene in her mind, she thought,
of course he was impatient and arrogant even then, but I
was so infatuated that I didn't realise it. Why didn't I tell
anyone about the marriage? It would have been easy
enough then. And the answer came to her, it was because
she didn't want anyone else to interfere or to shatter her
lovely dream. But was the dream made up of illusion?

At last the sound of thunder diminished to a far away
muttering and the lightning ceased to light up her room in
bright flashes. To the sound of the rain, regular and soothing now, at last Perry slept.

CHAPTER FOUR

It was still raining next morning when Shadrac brought in her breakfast, golden porridge made from crushed Indian corn and a woven basket of delicious fruits, pale lichees, pink guavas and bright orange mangoes. A mug of strong coffee made her feel lively and wide awake, ready to face the problems that beset her. When she arrived downstairs, Tarquin was there already and she thought he eyed her clean blue jeans and tailored blue and white striped cotton shirt rather ironically.

'You're likely to get muddy again today,' he informed her. 'I'll need your help in a rescue operation. The river is still coming down and there are various animals trapped upon islands in the middle of the floods, so we'll have to try to get them off. Have you eaten? Good. We can go as soon as Darrell arrives. Meanwhile I'll hitch the towbar on to the car. We'll have to take the motor launch. I've had to send the Africans off on another job, so it will be just us three. If Darrell arrives before I get back, tell him to hang on. We'd better all stick together and have a uniform plan for this operation.'

He had not even asked her whether she wanted to go with them, just commandeered her help as if he took it for granted, thought Perry, as she watched him stride to his Land Rover and drive off down the road. Well, she supposed, it would be less boring than hanging around in the house.

'You'll find waterproofs in the cloakroom in the hall,' he had shouted as he drove away.

There were numerous pieces of camouflaged raingear, heavy capes and sou'westers, and she was busy sorting them out and trying to find a small cape when she heard someone at the door.

It was Darrell, Lorraine's husband, slightly older, but still a handsome tough-looking ranger, with his shock of blond curly hair and his direct blue eyes, eyes that were looking at her now with smiling recognition.

'Why, aren't you little Perry, old Vaughan's grand-daughter? Long time no see. What on earth are you doing back here?'

Looking at Darrell's handsome, suntanned face, Perry experienced a great wave of relief. Here was someone, a normal person, who at last recognised who she was. She had begun to feel as if she were invisible with all the puzzling strangeness that she had encountered first with Tarquin and then with Lorraine. Now at last here was someone who remembered her previous visit.

'So you do know me! Tell me, Darrell, have I changed a great deal?'

Darrell laughed in the hearty way she remembered from that time before.

'Hardly at all. You've grown up quite a bit. You were a pretty child in those days and now you're a beautiful woman. Let's see, how long is it since you were here before?'

'Five years.'

'As long as that? How time flies! But a lot has happened since then. Five years, eh? That must have been just before Tarquin had his accident.'

'His accident? I didn't know he'd had an accident.'

'Oh, well, it must have been after you left. He was thrown from his horse and had very bad concussion. It was touch and go—he nearly didn't make it. But he's a tough one, is old Tarquin. Funny you didn't know about it, because it must have been around the time you went home. You remember you came on that trail with us, and it was the last one that Tarquin was ever able to lead. It was shortly after that that it happened.'

Perry felt like someone who has been groping in a dark passage and at last sees a glimmer of light in front of them, not much, but something that might lead to a better comprehension of the situation.

'But what happened ... I mean, when Tarquin had the accident?'

'An African found him by the side of the path leading to the house. He must have been lying there for some time. The African thought he was dead. In fact he was hardly breathing. By chance Lorraine had come to the house and she put him in an estate car, making him as comfortable as possible, and took him straight to hospital. It probably wasn't the right thing to do, but it would have been difficult to get a doctor to come here.'

'I wonder why my grandmother never told me about this,' mused Perry.

'Ah, now, it's coming back. I remember something about that. Your grandmother said you were not to be worried because she thought you'd been fond of Tarquin, and wasn't there something about your aunt being in hospital at the time?'

'Yes, I suppose that was it.'

She remembered how her grandparents had always treated her as a child. It was just like Grandma not to want to give her bad news about someone they knew she liked.

'He made a wonderful recovery, but it changed him somewhat. Bad concussion does that sometimes. Have you noticed?'

'Yes, I do think he seems different,' Perry said slowly.

'The thing that seems to have worried him most, and I can tell you he's very touchy about it, is that the accident seemed to leave great blanks in his memory. He doesn't remember much of what happened before he was thrown, but if you try to tell him anything, he blows his top. He seems to be particularly sensitive about that time in his life. He hated being ill and he seems to want to forget it. He won't have it that he has these blank spots, but I know he has. You just don't have to let him know you realise he can't remember much of the past.'

'So that accounts for it! It puzzled me because he doesn't seem to remember me at all,' Perry told him.

'Well, there you are, you see. That proves what I'm saying.'

'Please don't tell him you recognised me,' Perry asked quickly. 'If he's sensitive about it, he won't like to be reminded. I've already told him I've been here before, but he just said so did hundreds of others.'

'Yes, that's true, it was a very thriving prosperous outfit until this happened. But after that, Tarquin seemed to lose interest in having visitors to the camps. He seemed to become a bit of a recluse. Perhaps we shouldn't have left him at that time, but I was offered a better job with the National Parks and with the visitors gone there was not as much work here, and I must say Tarquin was rather depressing company at that time. He was like a lost soul, or perhaps rather like a person who's lost something that he knows he can't replace. He really was most strange. Lorraine was very good to him at the time of the accident, but eventually she became very bored here, so we opted out. Maybe it was not the right thing to do, for here we are back again because I contracted malaria and needed an easier post.'

'Perhaps it will be good for Tarquin to have you and Lorraine around once more,' Perry suggested.

Darrell looked at her doubtfully.

'Maybe you're right. There was a time when I thought that Lorraine ... oh, well, forget it. I know this life is rather boring for a girl like Lorraine and she misses the bright lights. She's not cut out for a ranger's wife, not unless the ranger should be wealthy as well to allow her to lead a luxurious life and travel sometimes to see some other parts of the world.'

Perry wondered whether he was referring indirectly to Tarquin and she felt sorry for him. She put out her hand and touched him.

'Well, she's still with you, isn't she? Promise me, Darrell, that you won't say a word to Tarquin about knowing who I was, not even to Lorraine. She only met me once and doesn't seem to know me. I don't want to upset him if I have to stay here for goodness knows how long.'

'That's a bargain,' said Darrell. 'You can choose your own time for telling him or keep quiet if you wish to. It's all the same to me. I agree with you it would be foolish to upset him over such a little thing. You always were a sweet kid, Perry.'

She was still holding his hand and now he leaned forward and gave her a light kiss.

'That's a promise, then. Thank you, Darrell.'

There was a sound at the door and there stood Tarquin. He eyed them and his twisted smile made Perry think he had witnessed the kiss, but all he said was, 'Come along now, we have no time to lose. The river is rising again and I want to reach those islands before it does.'

As they drove, sliding and skidding over the muddy road that led to the river, Perry tried to think over the significance of Darrell's information. Part of the puzzle was solved. She remembered, oh, so vividly, that last sight of Tarquin, riding away on the rough track, going hell for leather, as if some friend were after him. That must have been when the accident happened, minutes after he had left her, and she had spent all these bitter years thinking that he had deserted her because he had tired of her. When she had phoned before she went to the airport, he must have been already on his way to the hospital, driven by Lorraine. The African servant had tried to tell her. She remembered how he had said something about 'Not good', but she had not understood, and she had been eaten up, consumed with jealousy because she thought Tarquin had gone on some lighthearted jaunt with Lorraine, when all the time ... oh, how could fate have treated her so badly?

And now? He had forgotten her entirely. She meant less than nothing to him. Five long years had intervened, five years in which, let's face it, she had eaten out her heart for him, or rather for the man he had once been, and yet, as far as he was concerned, she might never have existed. But what could she do now? How to announce to a man who thought he had never met her before that she might or might not have been married to him and now wanted to know for sure in order to gain her freedom from any possible ties with him and marry another man? Would he even believe her? But why should she invent such an astounding tale? And yet with his deep distrust of women that the television interview and its consequences seemed to have generated, she felt the chances of his taking her story seriously were certainly not good.

The rain was still dripping down from a sullen grey sky. Was this the Africa she had known? And yet a steamy heat seemed to rise from the damp ground and the pungent smell of exotic vegetation was all around them. In the heavy borrowed rain cape and waterproof hood, Perry felt uncomfortably hot. Tarquin, she noticed, had not equipped himself with these things. His hair was sculptured to his head in dark curls, like some Michelangelo statue, and the green ranger's shirt clung to his pectoral muscles like a second skin. Quietly she slipped out of the enveloping raincoat. That was better. The warm rain bathed her like a comforting shower, and soon the striped shirt was as wet and clinging as Tarquin's and her hair fell in a miniature waterfall over her shoulders.

They followed a muddy trail above the course of the swollen river until they reached a place where the course of the waters divided leaving some islands in the wide expanse. They had been towing a motor launch behind the Land Rover and now Tarquin and Darrell unhitched it.

'We'll have to manage this on our own,' Tarquin said. 'I had to send the available Africans on another task. Anyway, we may need all the room we can get in the boat itself and Perry is smaller than an African ranger.'

'And much more attractive company,' said Darrell, smiling.

Tarquin frowned as if he disapproved of this remark and Perry hoped frantically that Darrell hadn't forgotten his promise not to betray their previous acquaintance.

'You must wear a life jacket,' Tarquin told her, and he handed her a rather cumbersome garment of bright orange.

'Oh, must I? It's so hot,' Perry protested.

'Of course. The boat's pretty safe, but I'm not risking the life of a woman visitor. Think of the bad publicity we'd get.'

Is that all he cares about? thought Perry. Just the adverse publicity the Reserve would get if there was an accident to a visitor here? That's all my life matters to him now. She struggled with the intricate lacing of the life jacket.

'Let me help you,' said Darrell, helping her to put the lacing into the right holes.

'Oh, thank you so much, Darrell. I haven't got much experience of these things.'

Another frown from Tarquin. Did he think she had got on first name terms with the other man too easily? He was watching Darrell's clumsy fingers fumbling with the life jacket over the clinging wetness of her shirt front. How could she help it if it looked too intimate? Darrell was only being kind, and with him she felt as impersonal as if she were in a doctor's surgery.

'Don't take all day over that, Darrell, however much you may be enjoying it,' snapped Tarquin.

Darrell looked surprised, as well he might, thought Perry.

'Come along now, we've no time to lose. Perry, you sit at that end. Have we got all the equipment, Darrell? Make yourself useful, Perry, and stow some of it under the seats.'

'Why didn't Lorraine come to help?' asked Perry, stung to ask this by Tarquin's arrogant commands.

Both of the men laughed and Darrell said, 'Lorraine? Good grief, this isn't her scene.'

'Then why me, for heaven's sake?'

'We had to have somebody and it stands to reason you must be fairly practical, if you made your way here on your own in a borrowed car. You give the impression of efficiency, wouldn't you say, Darrell?'

Said in that tone of voice, it hardly seemed a compliment.

'Oh, rather,' Darrell agreed. 'I remember she was. . . .'

His voice trailed away and he looked sheepish as Perry shot him a warning glance, but Tarquin was busy with the boat and did not seem to notice his slip.

The river had recovered somewhat from the torrential deluge of yesterday, but here, where there were wide sand-banks, it had broadened into the appearance of a wide small lake. Flung up on the banks there were all kinds of debris, branches of trees, pathetic remains of birds' nests, round pumpkins wrested from African lands higher up the stream and sad small bodies of animals that had been caught by the flood waters.

'How do you know there's anything trapped on the islands?' asked Perry.

To her there seemed to be no movement there, only the wind in the reeds, swaying the nests of the weaver birds that hung where they had wisely built them high above the stream.

'Sure to be,' said Tarquin cryptically. 'It's just a fact of life.'

And as the boat chugged its way towards the biggest of the strips of land, Perry became aware of several antelopes among the trees. They were staring at the craft, just as cows or sheep stare at a strange object in a field, but, as the boat came nearer, they retreated back, trying to find a more secure hiding place.

'You stay here, Perry,' Tarquin commanded, as he flung a rope around an overhanging tree and steadied the boat. 'Be ready to start the boat if we run into difficulties.'

'But couldn't I be useful to you if I came with you?'

'You might, but I daren't risk it. There are probably snakes there and you haven't got the boots for it.'

Perry noticed now that they were both wearing high boots and carrying sticks as well as rifles, and for the first time she had qualms of nervousness about the dangers of this expedition that seemed from their attitude to be quite commonplace.

'Look out for hippos,' added Tarquin. 'If one comes too near for comfort, start the boat. The noise might drive it away. Here's a whistle. Blow it if you need us. We won't be far away.'

Then they disappeared into the thick bush on the island and Perry was left alone. It was too quiet. The sound of lapping water, the lonely call of a bird high over the river, the sullen weeping grey of the sky, so different from the usual dazzling blue of Africa, all depressed her spirits. In the light of Darrell's revelation, what was she to do about her situation?

Tarquin was now like a total stranger, not even friendly

towards her, and in his present state of mind he was entirely ignorant of the events of that long-ago vacation. But what now if she tried to do it alone? The thought suddenly struck her that she might make the journey to that mission beyond the Game Reserve, possibly find the priest who had performed the ceremony and get to the truth through him. She would have to find out if there was another way of getting to the place. Certainly she would not be able to do it on her own through the wilderness. But if there was a road?

Her thoughts were suddenly interrupted by a shout from the bank.

'Look out, Perry, there's a bushbuck coming your way. Start the engine. We must head him to the shore.'

Tarquin was suddenly there again, springing into the boat with an agility surprising for such a large man.

'Good girl, it's started first time. Now look out for the beast. Darrell's heading it this way towards us.'

He was at her side, his arm warm against her own as he took the wheel, the bulk of him imprisoning her body in the narrow seat. No, it was impossible. How could she feel any longer a physical response to this man who had become a stranger? She tried to shake off the wild delight she felt at this close accidental nearness, but she could feel her pulses beating rapidly and her unruly heart throbbed in her breast.

There was a shout from Darrell and an animal, that seemed to Perry nearly as big as a horse, leapt from the bank into the water. She could see, beneath the beautiful antlers, the huge frightened eyes as the animal began to swim, desperately heading in wide circles, unable to find its direction. Tarquin steered the boat towards the terrified beast and kept beside it, guiding it to the shore. Its panic seemed to subside as it reached firm ground and stumbled up the bank. It shook itself and hastened towards the trees, the round white mark on its rump showing distinctly while the rest of its dun pelt had disappeared from view.

As they approached the island again, a flurry of smaller animals leapt into the water driven by Darrell, red-gold impala, huffing and puffing with deep noisy grunts as they struggled against the current.

'They'll be all right,' said Tarquin. 'It's just a question of getting them going. Most animals can swim, but a lot of them would rather not.'

Several warthogs were rooted out, running in ludicrous panic, their tails held high like little flags, and a few wildebeeste stampeded crazily towards the water. Again these had to be guided towards the bank and Perry watched them executing wild acrobatic jumps as they left the river on the farther side, their bodies seeming out of all proportion to their heads with the grotesque Roman nose profiles.

Every now and again, Darrell or Tarquin would appear and thrust into Perry's hands some smaller kind of animal, tiny antelope with minute horns, and she would put them into sacks and take them across the water, then gently release them. After a while they seemed to have cleared the island.

'That's finished, then,' said Tarquin. 'We'll go to another one.'

'It was dead easy,' Perry commented. 'No snakes, no hippos, no buffalo.'

'Don't speak too soon. We still have to clear the other island.'

'Are buffalo dangerous?' asked Perry. 'In pictures they look rather mild creatures.'

'Deadly,' said Darrell. 'More dangerous than a lion, treacherous and determined. I'd sooner face a croc than an angry buffalo.'

'And speaking of crocs, look at that,' said Tarquin.

Perry gasped. On a sandspit, very close to the place

where he was tying the boat up, lay an enormous crocodile, about fourteen feet long. It lay as still as a log, but its slits of eyes seemed to move slightly as it heard the noise of the boat.

'That's bad,' said Darrell. 'If it hasn't fed, it'll be after the animals we sent into the water.'

'What of it?' Tarquin told him. 'It has to eat.'

Perry felt exasperated by his cool common sense.

'I don't understand you,' she cried. 'Here you are going to infinite trouble to rescue these animals from the islands and you don't care if that horrible crocodile eats them!'

'It won't eat the lot. It will be satisfied with one. What typical feminine logic that you're sorry for pretty creatures like impala but not for the crocodile which needs a meal. I haven't noticed that you refuse meat—well, neither does the crocodile.'

'You aren't going to leave me in this boat with that creature staring at me, are you? Please let me come on to the island?'

'Certainly not. You have your whistle, haven't you? If you feel in any danger, just blow it. We'll only be a couple of hundred yards away. There might most certainly be much more danger on the island than there is for you staying in a boat with a croc fifty feet away from you. It isn't in the least interested in you anyway. It would much rather have a fat little antelope. Your job is to drive the boat if you see any animals being swept away. You're on your own now. I must stay with Darrell.'

So she had to stay, and again she wondered why she had had the crazy idea that she must come here herself to solve her problem. This man, whom she thought she had once married, was quite impossible. And she had thought she could talk to him sanely and sensibly! But that had been when she was in London. Things didn't seem quite as clear-cut in Africa. She looked at the crocodile and it seemed to her that its cynical smile mirrored her own thoughts.

Tarquin and Darrell seemed to be being kept busy. Quite a few animals, driven by their shouts, appeared on the bank and made for the water, but the crocodile did not stir. Perhaps it, had eaten its fill of the creatures already drowned. Perry, on her own now, kept starting the boat and driving the animals to the other bank, and, to her relief, the crocodile took no interest in the proceedings and she soon forgot about it.

Coming back to the place where she tethered the boat, she was interested to see a grey duiker, a small pretty doe, that had paused in the bushes and seemed reluctant to enter the water. It bleated softly and then she realised that it was calling, signalling to a baby duiker which now came stumbling on uncertain feet towards its mother. It must surely have been born on the island, the night before. How could a small creature like that possibly swim? Perry made up her mind that she would have to do something about it, provide help in some way. Tarquin had forbidden her to leave the boat, but she would only have to step ashore and go a few paces into the bush. The grey duiker might be able to run fast, but she was sure that the baby calf could not.

Making sure that the boat was securely fastened, she waded into the shallow water and hoisted herself up on to the bank. The grey duiker stared at her in alarm and hastily retreated deeper into the bush, but the baby lingered behind, gazing at her with wide innocent eyes. Cautiously Perry edged towards it. She had taken the precaution of bringing a net from the equipment in the boat and now she threw it over the little creature and drew it gently towards her. It seemed paralysed with fright and did not stir as she withdrew the net and cradled it in her arms. The mother's soft calls became bleats of alarm, but Perry hardened her heart to this. She must get this small scrap over to the other side together with its mother. If she took the baby, she felt sure the parent would follow.

She deposited the little animal in the bottom of the boat, where it started calling softly and rather pathetically like the small mews of a newborn kitten. As she started the engine, she watched the shoreline and saw the adult duiker emerge from the bush and stand upon the shore turning its head and pawing the sand in an agitated way.

'Sorry, my dear, it's only for your own good,' she told her, as she edged cautiously into deeper water. And then, to her great relief, she saw the animal enter the river and start swimming strongly after the boat. She was halfway across and congratulating herself on the success of her plan, when suddenly some sixth sense made her look for the crocodile. It had been immobile for so long that she had tended to ignore the danger. Having got over her first fear of it, and now that it seemed uninterested in her operations with the animals, she had begun to think of it as almost as harmless as a log of wood upon the spit of land that lay between the animals and the safe further bank.

But that glance towards it made her freeze with horror. For a moment she felt as paralysed with fear as the little duiker had been when it found itself in the net. With slow ungainly waddle it was slithering towards the edge of the sandspit and its ugly snout was turned in the direction of the swimming grey duiker. Perry turned the nose of the boat and accelerated, but she could not go too fast or she would lose the animal that was following in the wake of the boat. But she must get away, go further downstream than she had gone before, if she wanted to shake off the croc's attentions.

She headed in a diagonal direction upstream hoping that the mother would not be too exhausted to follow. She could see the croc hesitating on the edge of the sandspit. Was it considering whether it was worthwhile to pursue a fast disappearing prey? Then she saw it slide into the water and vanish in the muddy swirls. How fast could a crocodile swim? She had no idea.

She steered towards the bank, expecting that at any moment she would see the head of the crocodile emerge beside the frantically swimming duiker and see it dragged under water. But she managed to reach the other side with the animal still paddling after her. She beached the boat and, as soon as the mother emerged without mishap, she released the little one. She had been half afraid that the mother would disown the calf because of the human smell upon it, but, as soon as they were reunited, it began to lick its young one all over and then bounded into the bush with the baby after it, apparently none the worse for its experience.

And now for the return journey. In her anxiety to get as far away from the croc as possible, she had come much further down river than she had intended, and the current was now against her. Added to that, the crocodile was somewhere in these waters, presumably heading towards her and deprived of its intended meal. Could crocodiles overturn a boat of this size? She thought of the huge length of the beast and the lash of its tail as it reached the water. Of course it could. She would not stand a chance if it chose to attack her.

And suddenly, right in midstream, with waves pounding against the sides of the boat, the engine spluttered and was silent. What to do now? She was much too far away from the island. The men might not even hear if she used the whistle or called for help. She struggled frantically to restart the engine, but it gave a faint splutter and then lapsed into silence. Further downstream a group of hippos surfaced and regarded her vessel with curious piggy eyes. What had Tarquin said about hippos? That they might overturn a boat if they were disturbed. She wished desperately that she had stuck to the simple short route from the island to the other bank and not let her sympathy for the duiker and its baby run away with her. But I couldn't have left it for the crocodile, she reasoned. I wonder what's become of the horrible beast. I wish I could see it safely snoozing on its sandbank.

There was a shout from the island and she could see Tarquin and Darrell on the shore. They were waving their arms.

'Come back!'

Faintly she heard Tarquin's commanding voice above the noise of the water pounding against the boat. She put her hands to her mouth to increase the volume.

'I can't,' she shouted. 'The engine has failed.'

'There are some oars in the bottom of the boat. Use them.'

She reached down for them and managed to get them into the rowlocks and started to try to propel them, but it was heavy going and the boat didn't seem to move more than an inch at a time.

'Hang on. I'll swim across,' Tarquin shouted.

'But the crocodile. . . .'

Perry's voice seemed to be carried away by the wind, because he took not the slightest notice of her warning but took off his shirt and dived into the water. She watched him swimming with strong overarm strokes, covering the distance in an incredibly swift time, but at each moment she expected to see him throw up his arms and go under, just as she had thought would happen to the duiker. She thought she had never felt so scared in all her life, but soon she was to be even more terrified.

There was a sudden alarmed shout from Darrell and, turning from her sight of Tarquin swimming against the current, she saw that a hundred yards away the crocodile had surfaced. She hoped desperately that it had not seen

Tarquin and would head in the direction of the sandbar, but it was not to be. The huge creature, the same colour as the turbulent river, started heading straight for the boat. It was as if it had decided to cut across Tarquin's route and it seemed as if man and beast must meet each other in midstream. She began to bang impotently against the side of the boat with an oar, but still the crocodile came on. By now Tarquin must have become aware of his danger, but he was nearer to the boat than the shore and he ploughed doggedly on through the water that seemed to Perry to be becoming increasingly tough. The crocodile was gaining on him now. It seemed impossible that Tarquin could reach the boat before they met. Someone was screaming now, high, short, desperate screams. Perry was totally unaware that the sounds were coming from her own throat.

And then, across the water, echoing over the sandy flats, came the report of a gun. Nothing happened, and now the crocodile was only about twenty-five yards from Tarquin and he still had another ten yards to cover. The beast's mouth was open as it closed for the kill. Two more shots rang out in quick succession, and this time they found their mark, into the tender region of the mouth and the under-belly that had been raised momentarily above the waves. The beast sank down in a flurry of bloody foam and Tarquin heaved himself over the gunwale of the boat and slapped Perry hard across the face.

'Stop that screaming! It doesn't help any and besides, the panic's over now. Come along, let's see what's wrong.'

Perry sat down quickly, nursing her stinging cheek. Her throat was tight and dry and sore and she felt utterly exhausted by the sensations of the last few minutes.

'I thought ... I thought the crocodile was going to get you,' she gasped out, her voice sounding to herself like an unrecognisable croak.

'Yes, it was a close call. But Darrell's a reliable shot and your little hysteria act might have slowed it down a bit, I'll say that for you. But what the devil were you doing so far down the river?'

He was examining the engine while he spoke and he gave a short angry laugh.

'I don't suppose it occurred to you that, with all the trips you've made to and fro, you might have run out of fuel? There's a can right here for just such emergencies.'

In a few moments the engine was restarted and they were heading for the shore.

'You didn't answer my question,' said Tarquin. 'What were you doing so far down river?'

He isn't going to like this any better than he's liked anything else about me in the last few minutes or, come to that, in the last two days, thought Perry.

'There was a duiker with a young calf,' she explained hesitantly. 'I knew the calf wouldn't be able to swim—it was only about a day old. So I went ashore and caught it.'

'You what? I thought I told you not on any account to leave the boat.'

'It was only for a few minutes,' she protested.

'I don't care how long it was for. Your job was to look after the boat. Suppose it had drifted away and we'd been marooned on that island?'

'I tied it securely before I left it. I caught the baby and started to take it across and the mother followed, but then I noticed the crocodile moving into the water, so I went further down river instead of straight across.'

'What the hell did one grey duiker matter compared with the possible loss of the boat? All I told you to do was to make the simple trip backwards and forwards across the river, not traipse to hell and gone down stream just for the sake of one baby antelope which might probably be dead before nightfall. And coming ashore too! You might quite easily have been bitten by a green mamba. We saw several of them hanging from the trees and their bite is fatal—or didn't you know?'

'All right, maybe I didn't do things your way, but not everyone can be as hardhearted as you. I couldn't let that mother and baby die if there was any chance of saving them.'

'And then you wonder why I think women are unrealistic! This is Africa, girl, not some nice Sunday School picnic.'

'All right, it's Africa. So why didn't you leave all those animals to find their own way off the islands?'

He didn't even bother to reply to her as they collected Darrell from the island and headed for the opposite shore.

'Pity about that croc,' he said to Darrell. 'You had to do it, of course, but there aren't so many of those big fellows left in this part of the river, and they're essential for the ecology of the place. We'll find ourselves over-stocked with barbel if we kill too many crocs, because the barbel eel is the croc's favourite food.'

'It looked for a moment as if you were due to be that crocodile's favourite food,' said Perry drily.

He hasn't even thanked Darrell for saving his life, she thought, dumbfounded. Just regrets that the croc had to be shot. Wasn't that typical?

CHAPTER FIVE

By the time they arrived back at the house, the shadows were lengthening and the evening scent of wild jasmine wafted across the clearings.

'Phone Lorraine and tell her to come over for dinner,' Tarquin told Darrell. 'She can bring some clean clothes for you and you can shower here. You deserve a drink for saving my life today. We'll kill a bottle of whisky and the girls can drink champagne.'

So he had appreciated Darrell's shooting the crocodile, yet Perry wondered whether he didn't want to be alone with her any more than was necessary. Doubtless Lorraine would dress elegantly for dinner even in the wilderness. Perry looked over the contents of her suitcase and choose a dress of a woven mixture of finest mohair and pure silk in a rich creamy colour that enhanced the gold of her hair. It was very simply cut with a low neckline held up by narrow straps and she added a topaz pendant on a thin gold chain and a bracelet with links of gold. She twisted her hair into a simple pleat at the back of her head, achieving an air of much more sophistication than when she wore it on her shoulders.

Why, she wondered, was she making this effort? Tarquin would hardly notice what she looked like. Pride, she thought. Lorraine looks so glamorous even in these wild surroundings, so I must try to look good to. But for whom? She shied away from the idea that she was still attracted to

Tarquin. That moment of physical contact in the boat had not really meant anything. It was just that the whole situation had been exciting. That was why her heart had pounded and her knees felt like candles, when he had sat beside her pressed against her merely because of the narrow confines of the boat.

If we had stayed together when I was very young, she thought, maybe I could have tolerated his arrogance. But not now. What am I to do about it? She hated the thought of going back to Sinclair and confessing failure. If only she could find some way to travel to the African village and investigate the legality of that ceremony on her own!

When she came down, Lorraine was already there, busily arranging a mossy dish of wild orchids for a table decoration. She eyed Perry up and down, obviously intensely interested in her appearance.

'You're looking very well dressed for a small dinner party in the bush,' she remarked in sweetly sour tones.

She herself was certainly anything but plainly dressed. She was wearing a dress of almost Spanish appearance with large bright scarlet and green flowers against a dark background, frills and flounces at the hem and at the deeply plunging neckline, and the effect was enhanced by a scarlet hibiscus in the dark hair that was parted in the centre and drawn into a large coil at the nape of her neck.

'Your flower arrangement looks very beautiful,' said Perry, rather at a loss for something to say.

'I usually try to add a feminine touch when Tarquin entertains. Shadrac does wonders. He's very well trained, but there's always something missing when a man lives alone, even one as self-sufficient as Tarquin, don't you agree?'

'Yes, I suppose so, but he must have had to do without these feminine touches for some years while you were away, mustn't he?'

'We were not entirely at the other end of the world, you know. We always kept in touch.'

Perry wondered whether this was a way of warning her off, of informing her that Lorraine was still interested in Tarquin.

'There have been many women, of course, who would have welcomed the opportunity to persuade Tarquin away from his bachelor establishment, but they have never succeeded. He dislikes most women even if he can be physically attracted to the odd few. What man can't?'

Yes, I'm definitely being warned off, thought Perry.

She watched Lorraine's slender hands with their catlike nails, glossy with opalescent polish, bending the frail orchid blossoms to go the way she willed them, and she remembered how she had felt, long ago, when she had seen those ivory-coloured hands hold on to Tarquin so possessively.

'The television interview was a great mistake,' Lorraine continued. 'Tarquin doesn't realise the extent of his attraction for women and he was utterly surprised and disgusted at the response to his appearance. Women who wanted to make his acquaintance have been quite shameless in the way they've gone about it. But I must say, he's usually succeeded in sending them about their business. He's never had to have anyone actually staying here with him before.'

'You mean as I am?' said Perry, stung to reply but trying hard to keep her temper.

Lorraine shrugged.

'If the cap fits ... ?' she sneered.

'I can assure you that as soon as I can cross the causeway, nothing will give me greater pleasure than to leave this place and everyone in it. I'm not one of the women who find Tarquin devastating. To me he seems arrogant, conceited and damned rude most of the time.'

'And the rest of the time?' asked Lorraine. She eyed

Perry meaningfully. 'You don't mean to tell me that the elegant dress and adornments are for the benefit of the monkeys? You can't fool me. I've had too much experience of the way women try to fascinate Tarquin, but let me tell you, Perry, you'll never get him. He's just not interested in you. He told me so himself.'

Perry was saved a reply by the arrival of the men. Perhaps they had had some of the promised whisky. Certainly they were both in a convivial mood, both laughing and both mocking each other in friendly fashion. Up to now it seemed to Perry that she had only seen Tarquin at his worst, but now, with a kind of hurt feeling somewhere deep inside her, she sensed again his well remembered charm. She accepted a glass of pale golden sherry and sat there trying to prevent her eyes being drawn to the face of this laughing stranger who once had been so dear to her. Tarquin, Darrell and Lorraine had the easy intimacy of long friendship, and tonight she felt on the outside, an interloper gazing over a high barrier at a life she could not share.

After dinner they moved on to a patio, high above the surrounding wilderness. It was the place that in previous days favoured visitors had used as a lookout, and below was a waterhole, illuminated now by the light of the moon. The clouds of the day had vanished and above them the sky was a deep cobalt blue lit by huge stars like silver flowers blossoming all over the heavens. Dappled by moonlight and scarcely distinguishable in the light and shade, a group of zebras drank deeply, then galloped nervously away, and in the trees vervet monkeys, disturbed by the commotion, argued sleepily together, then lapsed into muttered grumbling. A flock of ibis winged in, black against the moon, calling their loud 'ha-de-dah' before they settled in the shallows.

'Not much game tonight,' said Tarquin. 'The animals have been disturbed by the floods, and of course they don't need to come here in search of water. There's plenty, too much in fact, all around the wilderness area.'

'How long do you expect it will take for the waters to subside?' asked Perry.

'Anyone's guess. It sometimes takes a week or more. These rains this morning have been heavier up country. The rivers will be fuller still tomorrow.'

'That doesn't sound a very cheerful prospect,' commented Perry.

'Are you bored by our company already—and yet you came so many miles to visit us?'

In the half darkness of the moonlit patio, Perry could see the flashing white of Tarquin's mocking smile. All around her was the swooning fragrance of the datura lilies, their huge white trumpets outlined against the darkness of the leaves. Sleepy doves murmured among the bushes near at hand and she remembered Tarquin had told the young girl she had been how they constantly lament their lost love, 'I have lost my husband and my heart goes doo-doo-doo-doo.'

'Not bored,' she told him. 'One could hardly rate today's events as boring.'

'We must see if we can provide some more excitement for you,' said Darrell.

'Not the kind we had today,' Perry protested.

'What the hell,' said Tarquin. 'Darrell's a good shot and obviously my time hadn't come in spite of your little oversight about the fuel.'

Perry wished that he had not brought that up again, specially in front of Lorraine, who laughed and putting her hand possessively on Tarquin's knee, said, 'You can't expect Perry to be all that clued up about things in the wilds. She comes from London and isn't she dying to get back! I suspect she has a much more civilised boy-friend than she could find around here.'

Tarquin frowned, but Darrell laughed and asked, 'Have you, Perry?'

His manner was too intimate, thought Perry, for someone who was only supposed to have met her today. She wished he would be more careful.

'Wouldn't you like to know?' said Lorraine, saving Perry from a reply, and, turning to Tarquin, she added, 'Darrell seems to have taken quite a shine to your visitor, Tarquin. Better be careful or he'll be higher than you in the popularity stakes.'

How on earth could she speak about her own husband like that, thought Perry, even if it was her idea of a joke?

It was an hour or so later over a last nightcap just before they were to go that the subject of the morrow was broached.

'You'll have to start early if you're to do that long trip in one day,' said Tarquin, who had been talking to Darrell.

'I know it. It's quite a way and the roads will be a spot rough after the rains, but they're much better than they used to be,' he said, turning to Perry as if he were giving her information. Fortunately, she thought, he didn't add anything about 'When you were here before,' as he might well have done.

'Where are you going to?' she asked, a wild idea beginning to form in her mind.

'Right across to the other side of the Reserve. There are no rivers to flood that way, but there've been heavy rains and Tarquin wants me to check up on various animals and see how they've fared.'

'Will you go on foot?' she asked.

'Good grief, no! We used to do it on foot when we ran wilderness trails for the tourists, but nowadays we take a truck. It's much quicker, of course. The African rangers will have done the investigations. It's just a matter of checking up on their reports. I'll be following the road for most of the way. That way with luck it should only take a day though rather a long one. Would you care to come with me?'

She noticed that Tarquin gave a quick frown. Evidently he didn't exactly approve of Darrell's suggestion.

'Are you serious? Could I really come?'

Here, she thought, was a heaven-sent solution to her problem. Once they had set out she could possibly persuade Darrell to take her to the mission. It could not be much out of his way.

'Darrell will have a considerable amount of work to do. He doesn't need a woman's company to distract him,' said Tarquin.

She glanced quickly at him and saw that his bronzed face looked even darker and his mouth was set in a grim line. This made her even more determined to go.

'Of course she must go if she would like to,' said Lorraine, very sweetly.

This was a surprise. Perry had thought Lorraine would most certainly object to her going off with Darrell, but here she was complacently taking her side. Could it be that she wanted the two of them out of the way so she could have some time alone with Tarquin and was seizing this opportunity for her own ends?

'Won't you come too?' asked Perry.

It was the last thing she wanted to happen. She might persuade Darrell to go to the mission without any explanation, but certainly Lorraine would be more curious.

'Good heavens, no! It isn't my scene at all. But it's a good chance for you to see something of the Reserve provided that's what you want. You won't need a chaperon with my husband. I'll trust you with him for the day.'

'That's very generous of you,' Perry replied.

Tarquin, she could see, was still smouldering.

'So it's settled,' said Darrell, looking pleased. 'I'll be

glad of your company, Perry. Is that all right with you, Tarquin?'

'It seems I don't have much choice, if you have all decided Perry is to go.'

Lorraine slipped her hand through his arm and gazed up into his face with those beautiful dark eyes, looking, Perry thought, rather like a cat that had been offered minced fillet steak.

'If they're to have a good time, so can we. Don't worry, Tarquin. We'll look after each other. We often have, haven't we?'

It seemed to Perry that Lorraine was making a flagrant admission of her interest in Tarquin, but Darrell seemed to ignore it. Possibly he was used to it.

Shortly afterwards the other couple took their leave.

'Get Shadrac to wake you at four-thirty. We must be on our way by five,' Darrell instructed her.

'We don't have much room for guests. Otherwise you could have come with us now,' said Lorraine.

'You know you always say you can't be bothered with visitors,' said Darrell.

Lorraine pouted.

'Oh, I just meant for tonight. It's true, I hate extra work. Housekeeping for two people is quite enough for me. I don't have Tarquin's efficient staff.'

'You've never gone short of servants,' said Darrell, sounding piqued.

'But what servants!' exclaimed Lorraine. 'One Shadrac is worth ten untrained houseboys, and you know I don't like cooking.'

'Then you'd better eat lunch with me tomorrow,' Tarquin suggested.

'Oh, that will be divine. Why should Darrell and Perry be the only ones to enjoy themselves?'

'What I'm going to do tomorrow couldn't be exactly

classed as a luxury picnic,' Darrell protested. 'Bring a shady hat, Perry. The sun could be the ruin of that beautiful English skin.'

At last they were left alone and Tarquin turned to Perry.

'Care for some more coffee before we turn in?'

'Yes, please,' said Perry.

If I had any sense, I'd go straight up to bed, she thought. She felt in a strange mood, feverish and elated. The weird sound of the wilderness at night, sudden music of a bird, excited chattering of monkeys, the odd highpitched calling of the zebras, the shout of an eagle owl, all combined with a fragrance like that of gardenias, made her feel she would like to stay here high above the trees, until dawn broke over the forest. She was worlds away from the woman she had become, the sedate, cautious person who led her well ordered life in London. She was back again, breathing in the romance of Africa, thrilled once more by the strangeness of her surroundings and the velvety glamour of the starlit night.

And Tarquin was a dark presence, sensed rather than seen, yet, as she sipped her coffee slowly, she felt that he was gazing at her, just as she had known his penetrating glance when she had first met him and again during those few magical days in the wilderness that had led through passionate torment to those nights of high romance. She tried to throw off this feeling, throw off the intense excitement that Tarquin could still arouse in her.

He set down his coffee cup and she was reminded of that time when he had first kissed her. Then he crossed over to where she was sitting stiffly upright on the deep-cushioned bamboo couch. He put out his hand for her cup, but she clung to it as if it gave her some frail defence against him.

'You're taking a long time to finish your coffee,' he said, and took it from her grasp. 'Tell me, why this sudden attraction to Darrell? You positively threw yourself at him when he suggested the trip tomorrow.'

'There's no attraction,' she protested. 'I'm merely interested to see the wilderness again.'

'Ah, yes, you said you'd been here before, but I suspect this passionate interest in nature. Darrell's a good-looking guy and you two seemed to get on friendly terms remarkably quickly. Could it be that you're using this trip to the wilderness as an excuse for a quick romance?'

'In one day?' Perry said sharply. 'What nonsense! Lorraine didn't seem to object to my joining Darrell, so why should you?'

'Why indeed? Darrell's a nice guy. Why should I stop him having a little love on the side if he wants it?'

'That's absurd! You seem to have a very low opinion of me, Tarquin. But I assure you I have no interest in Darrell. Why, I hardly know him!'

'So what? I hardly know you, Perry, but it still doesn't prevent me feeling that physically you're a very attractive woman. Escape from an imminent death has made me feel amorous. You're looking very alluring tonight and you damned well know it.'

His hand was suddenly under her chin, holding her firmly so that she could not have got away if she had wanted to, and then he was kissing her, those deep penetrating kisses that she had known so often in her dreams. Now one hand was on the bare hollow of her back and the other smoothing the curve of her throat, reaching down to sweep the strap of her dress from her shoulder, caressing the gentle curves that lay beneath.

I mustn't feel like this, she told herself frantically, and then was swept along on a wave of such intense emotion that it seemed to block out all logical thought. Her mind seemed to stand aside, but her body, being stroked with gentle sensuality, appeared to recognise that this man, face shadowy and eyes mysterious in the dark of the patio, was no stranger to it. Against her will, it responded to caresses as familiar as if it had experienced them only yesterday. With a muttered exclamation Tarquin drew her to her feet and she stood there trembling, longing for his touch, the scent of lilies all around her.

'Where are we going to?' she stammered, as he started to lead her indoors.

'To my bed. Where else? Surely that's in your plan, you lovely enticing stranger?'

The word was like a shower of ice in the warm enchantment of the blue velvet night. Yes, that was all she was to him, a stranger who would be gone in a day or so, a person who was of no real importance to his life, someone who was good for a quick relief of the senses.

She tried to draw away from him but, as he held her close, she was made aware of the steel-like strength of his body and all at once she was desperately afraid both of him and of herself. She started to struggle, but was powerless in that great grasp.

'Having second thoughts? Surely not? Isn't this what you came for, so why shouldn't I make the most of it? And when you get back to London, you can tell your friends you slept with a game ranger in Africa. Won't they envy you your glamorous night?'

'I didn't come for that. You're totally mistaken to think so—and insufferably conceited as well!'

'Like most women, you're much more attractive when you're not talking,' he told her, and his mouth descended upon hers again, savagely demanding. Perry felt herself drowning in the depths of a warm, dark sea, and longed desperately to submit to the suffocating excitement that was sweeping her further and further from the shore. His mouth released her and she heard him murmur against the curve of her cheek, 'Lovely one, come to bed; we'll phone

Darrell and tell him you can't go with him tomorrow. I don't intend you should take that trip with him after spending the night with me.'

She managed to break away from him and, now that she was free of his touch, her mind ceased to be submissive to her body, though she could still feel the bruising touch of his hands.

'You'll do nothing of the sort,' she retorted. 'I have no intention of spending the night with you or of putting off that trip. I'm determined to go with Darrell tomorrow.'

His lean face was bright with anger.

'Why? You can't tell me after the last few minutes that you prefer him to me, or can it be that's just the way you react to any man who chooses to make love to you?'

'Maybe it is. You can think as you please. You seem to have a pretty low opinion of my morals even if you do want to make love to me. However, as far as I'm concerned, it's over now. I must go with Darrell tomorrow. I'm not going to change my plans.'

'Why are you so damned obstinate about it?' he demanded. 'What is Darrell to you? Could it be that you've met him before? You two seemed very matey right from the start. Could you have had an affair with him the last time you were here?'

How could she tell Tarquin the truth, the real reason why she wanted to do this journey with Darrell? Perry had to think quickly, to find some valid excuse.

'Darrell's not the reason I want to go. I want to do that article I spoke of. You said you had no objection so long as it didn't feature you.'

He looked at her doubtfully.

'Darrell has to hurry. You'll have very little time for photography. Why not leave it and I'll take you into the wilderness myself later.'

'That would be . . .'

Perry stopped. She had just been going to say, 'That would be heavenly!' How could she have had such a reaction?

'I think after the last few minutes I could hardly trust you during a trip into the wilderness,' she said.

That mocking smile again.

'No? Do you want to be able to trust me? Or is it that you can't trust yourself? You seemed interested enough in me a few minutes ago. Don't tell me that was all an act? Were you trying a seduction so you could write that up?'

Perry gasped.

'A seduction? You don't suggest it was I who was making love to you?'

'Hardly, but your responses were scarcely those of an affronted virgin, now were they? I thought you were, shall we say, rather eagerly co-operative. Could be that you wanted the experience for the sake of your journalistic efforts. It might make interesting reading for one of your women's magazines: "How to cope with an amorous game ranger in three easy lessons".'

'Oh, you really are insufferable!' she exclaimed.

'So why suffer me any longer? Since you're determined to go with Darrell (and good luck to the poor guy, because he'll need it) you had better get to bed. Don't bother to lock your door, I won't be coming your way tonight. I have no time for a woman who promises you gold and gives you sand.'

In spite of the lateness of the hour and the fact that she had to get up in a couple of hours' time, Perry lay sleepless for a long time. The living things of the night had ceased their wanderings and in the hours before dawn there was a kind of hush as if the wilderness held its breath. Only occasionally the creaky chirp of a cricket broke the silence and from somewhere in a treetop came the bell-like sound of a fruit bat, sweet and insistent.

Her body ached and on her mouth she could still feel the bruising sensation of Tarquin's kisses. His behaviour tonight had been utterly sadistic and yet, when she thought of him, it was as if a flame coursed through her. What am I to do now? she thought. Even though he made love to me, he seemed to regard me as an enemy. But tomorrow should unravel my problem. If I find, as I think will happen, that the marriage was illegal, he need never know anything about it. As soon as the road is clear, I can go back and never have to see him again. So why were the tears wet on her face and why was she feeling this sensation of dreadful, dull despair?

CHAPTER SIX

PERRY did not see Tarquin before she left next morning. Evidently Shadrac had been given instructions to wake her and provide coffee and rusks, for he knocked on her door at four-thirty exactly and she hastily drank some of the coffee though she could not eat.

'You're very punctual,' said Darrell when he saw her waiting on the front verandah of the house beside the tall white colonial columns. 'Why did you come out and stand in the dark? I could easily have rung the bell or rustled up Shadrac to fetch you.'

'I thought it best not to disturb Tarquin.'

'Like that, is it? He didn't seem too sold on the idea of your making this trip today, did he? That's the impression I got, and I know him pretty well.'

'I don't think he cares much what I do,' said Perry. 'He's only dying to get rid of me.'

'I can't think why,' Darrell said gallantly. 'If I were single like Tarquin and had a girl as beautiful as you dumped on me for a few days, I'd certainly make the most of it.'

He tried to, thought Perry.

'I've told him I'm a journalist and want to do an article about the Reserve and he's not too impressed,' she said.

'Are you really? But that's just what the place needs, a bit of favourable publicity so we can get more funds from the Parks Board. It's a hell of an expensive place to run as a private reserve. We need subsidising. Tarquin has plenty, but it's like pouring it down a bottomless pit. He's crazy not to have visitors any more. He used to enjoy it, showing everyone around, chatting up the girls. It's all changed since his accident.

And I was just one of the girls he chatted up, thought Perry, but in my case it went too far. She felt very thankful that she had come to her senses last night. If I had surrendered to temptation, she thought, I wouldn't be here now. But, try as she would, she could not banish from her imagination a picture of herself, waking in Tarquin's arms and beholding his sleeping face with gentle, tender passion as she had done all those years ago.

But it's not like that any more, she told herself sternly. If he touches me, he can still hold me bound by a desperate enchantment of the senses, but to him I'm just another woman to be taken because the opportunity is there. I myself mean nothing to him.

They were well on their way when the sun rising transformed the distant low hills to a lilac rose. From the high ridge where Tarquin had his house, the bush stretched for miles, dark and mysterious in the morning light, with patches of mist lying in the hollows where it was still damp with rain. Baboons on distant rocks barked away their fear of the night, and small auburn-pelted antelope lifted their heads to watch the truck pass, then trotted swiftly away through the dewy grass. Acacia trees flaunted their yellow blossom and the scent of them was heavy in the air.

If only this was Tarquin at my side, Perry found herself thinking, and then she told herself, don't be ridiculous. When you have thoughts like that, you're remembering the past. The Tarquin who wanted to take you to his bed last night was not at all related to the lover you once knew. There's no going back. I've lost Tarquin for ever. He no longer exists. Even the girl I was is locked away, lost somewhere in his injured mind. Of course you felt physical attraction. How could you not feel this when for five years you've dreamed of that former time? You thought you'd successfully put him out of your mind, but his touch can still thrill your senses. Well, it seems the only cure for that is to get away, to go home and never see him again, because you don't love him any more. How could you? He's so arrogant and he's cynical about women, more particularly about me. What would he think if I faced him with the truth? Would he even believe me? More and more she found herself wishing that she could prove the ceremony was illegal without having to resort to consulting Tarquin.

She had a lot of time for thoughts like these, because Darrell was not exactly a talkative companion and the business of inspecting conditions in the wilderness took longer than he had thought it would. Along the way there were round thatched huts, among clusters of aloes and surrounded by fences, where the African rangers led their rather lonely lives, posted there to warn off poachers and to see to the welfare of the animals in general. They had known by radio that Darrell was coming, so they were all at home, and every one of them wanted to engage Darrell in a long conversation.

'There's no hurrying an African,' Darrell told Perry. 'They have to tell a story at their own pace. The trouble is they all think time is no object. We're going to have to hustle to get through and get home before nightfall.'

Perry was dismayed. She saw the chances of going to the mission slipping away.

'Does it matter?' she asked. 'Do you usually do it in one day, or isn't there anywhere we could stay if it gets late?'

Darrell looked a bit startled.

'Well, yes, as a matter of fact I don't often manage the whole trip in a day. There's an old guest hut a few miles away, but it hasn't been used for ages, though we do leave blankets and tinned food there. It's rather rough, I'm afraid.'

This was where she could introduce her desire to go to the mission settlement, thought Perry swiftly.

'That time before, when we did the wilderness trail and I went on with Tarquin, I remember we stayed at a kind of African settlement for a few days. It can't be far from here. It was high above the river, and the elephants wandered along the bank below. It was so lovely, Darrell. Couldn't we go there for the night? The Africans were so charming and friendly and made us very welcome.'

'That's an idea,' said Darrell. 'I know of the place, of course, but I haven't been there for a long time. Still, there's no harm in trying. What's Tarquin going to say if you stay away for the night?'

Perry shrugged.

'He's welcome to think what he chooses. Will Lorraine mind?'

'Lorraine? Good heavens, no! She knows she can trust me. Didn't you hear her say you wouldn't need a chaperon?'

Lucky Lorraine, thought Perry. Still, she hardly thought she could come to much harm with Darrell. He was a real honest Joe. He wouldn't try to get her into his bed yet say he had no interest in her. She was safe with him.

They journeyed on along the gravelled track that had been hacked across the wilderness. Above them thorn trees stretched their flat tops to meet in an avenue of shade, and once Perry saw a tree with scarlet blossoms and a little sad-faced monkey reaching out small black hands to pull one of the bright clusters. Flocks of white egrets rose from the swampy ground around the waterholes that had been filled by the recent rains, and sometimes they saw white rhinos, a startling sight, huge, square-lipped, like prehistoric beasts.

The sun was setting, going down in a glorious tapestry of red and gold, when Perry thought there were landmarks that looked familiar.

'Isn't the mission somewhere near here?' she asked.

Her heart, that had seemed to slow down in the breathless heat of the day, now started to beat quickly. She felt a sensation of panic. So near now to the solution of the riddle! Fleetingly she faced the possibility that the African priest would not be there. Yet Africans stayed for ever if it was their home, didn't they? And even so there would be records.

'Just around the next bend,' Darrell promised her. 'I must say I'm looking forward to some of that lager we brought with us. There's a pool too, I think, where we might have a swim. No crocodiles there.'

'Yes, I remember,' Perry told him.

How could I forget? she thought. It was very secluded that pool, surrounded by rocks and overhanging ferns. We had it to ourselves and it was like being in the Garden of Eden. She remembered how, in the limpid water, Tarquin had touched the smooth silkiness of her skin and how they had embraced, intoxicated by the strangeness of those wet vibrant kisses. Where had it all gone, those beautiful shared sensations, that rapturous enchantment? Surely a ghost of them must linger around this place, exhaled in the heady perfume of the hot summer air?

They turned the last corner and she leaned forward eagerly. Whatever else happened, she had been happy here beyond her wildest dreams. Darrell braked suddenly and the truck skidded to a halt.

'Good lord!' he exclaimed. 'What on earth has happened?'

Perry gazed at the blackened ground, the charred remnants of what had been a community of neat thatched huts. Nothing remained. The church had gone too, that church where the young Africans had chanted her wedding songs. The blackened steeple sat with its bell among the shattered fabric of burned beams and ruined plaster.

'It must have occurred some time ago,' said Darrell. 'Look.'

Already in the blackened grass, red fire lilies were blossoming above the ruined ground.

'It's odd how a fire gets these things started,' Darrell told her. 'As if there's some desperate attempt at quick renewal. Well, that's it, then. We'd better get on to the guest hut.'

And he started up the engine.

'Wait,' said Perry.

In the ruins, she had detected a movement, and yes, an old African woman was there, prodding with a stick to see what she could find.

'Could we ask her what has happened to the people who were here before?' Perry asked Darrell. 'I liked the priest here and I want to know whether he came to any harm.'

'Very thoughtful of you,' said Darrell, and he called the old woman over to the car.

A long conversation followed. As Darrell had said before, the Africans like to make the most of a story, especially one as dramatic as this one. It is not in their nature to give news quickly. Perry did her best to be patient.

'Ask her where the priest has gone?' she asked.

'Does it matter?' said Darrell, looking rather surprised at this request. 'He's all right. He wasn't hurt. I expect he's been sent to some other church.'

'But where?' asked Perry, by this time feeling quite desperate.

Another long conversation followed.

'I didn't quite follow it all,' Darrell confessed finally. 'But it seems he's gone somewhere ... she doesn't know the name of the place, somewhere where there's a big lake.

There are many lakes to the north of here; it could be anywhere. At any rate he's alive and well and happy. Does it matter where he's living?'

'Can you ask her,' Perry said hesitatingly, 'did they manage to save anything?'

'She's already told me everything was burned, all the furniture, all their school books.'

Darrell was looking rather puzzled at Perry's insistence.

'And the church records? Please ask her, Darrell.'

He thinks I'm a bit crazy, thought Perry, but he usually does as he's asked. She heard him question the old woman again and saw her lift her hands level with her mouth and blow on them, then raise them in the air. Without translation, her meaning was clear.

'She says they were finished, gone with the wind.'

That night in the little guest hut, Perry faced and overcame the temptation to confide in Darrell. After the heat of the day, the night had turned cold and he had gathered some logs and lit a fire. In the warm light of the flames, it was easy to imagine telling her story to Darrell, who was so kind and reliable. She felt at her wits' end, and he knew Tarquin much better than she did. At least he knew this Tarquin who was so different from the one she thought she had known five years back. Darrell could give her advice. But something held her back. Mainly it was the long habit of secrecy that had grown up around the affair. She had been very reluctant to tell about it to Sinclair, so how could she confide in Darrell, who, however reliable he appeared, was married to Lorraine? Lorraine, she imagined, could worm any information out of any man.

So Perry kept her own counsel and considered the alternatives. All the evidence of the marriage was apparently gone and Tarquin had forgotten her very existence. So what was to stop her forgetting the whole thing and marrying whoever she chose? Nobody would ever know. Nobody had known about it anyway. Even if the marriage had been real, Tarquin did not remember it and the priest had gone to some unknown place in Africa, so she herself was the only one left.

But how can I live a lie? she thought desperately. I want to know. I can't be left like this, never knowing whether I have the right to marry again. And what about Sinclair? She knew he would never be satisfied until he knew the truth. So what can I do? And a small terrified voice inside her said, you'll have to tell Tarquin. There's nothing else for it. He'll know what to do. But he doesn't even like me now. Can he possibly believe me if I tell him such a fantastic tale? But what's the alternative? To commit myself to celibacy for the whole of my life since I can't marry not knowing whether that first one was real. If it was legal, I must try to have it annulled.

She was not sorry when next day Darrell made a rather leisurely journey back, because she still had not decided what was her best course of action. Somewhere along the line she had begun to come back to the previously despised idea that it would be better to return to England and leave the whole thing to Sinclair to sort out. At the moment she hated the idea of having to tell her story to Tarquin, and yet she had been here in Africa much longer than she had intended. How could she return to tell Sinclair she had found the problem insoluble? As yet Sinclair had never actually proposed marriage, but the fact that he had been so eager to help her solve her problem signified, she thought, that he was thinking about it.

'Thanks for your company, Perry,' said Darrell, when he dropped her at the house.

'Aren't you coming in? Won't Tarquin expect to see you?'

'No, no, I'll report to him tomorrow. It's pretty late and I must get back to Lorraine. She'll be holding back dinner for me. Mustn't keep the servants waiting.'

Perry let herself into the house and, in spite of everything, had a sensation of coming home. The gleaming copper, the glowing colours of the Persian rugs, the glossy woodwork, even the fierce lion rug were nostalgically familiar to her. If only the situation could have been different! Night comes early in Africa and already the lamps were lit, gleaming apricot gold from the spacious living room, where firelight from a crackling log fire flickered on the dark red leather chairs.

'Perry, is that you? Don't slip away upstairs. Come here where I can talk to you.'

Tarquin's harsh command shattered her tender memories of the house. It wasn't a place she loved and remembered well. It was his house, this arrogant, difficult stranger, who was standing there, the dark bulk of him silhouetted against the firelit room. To Perry his eyes seemed to have the dangerous golden glow of a wild creature beneath the thick black wings of his eyebrows. She felt a tremulous quiver of fear, then hardened herself to meet their fierce falcon gaze.

'So you've returned at last. Tell me, did you get good material for your article? You must have taken plenty of photographs, since you stayed away so long.'

'No, not many.'

'Really? You surprise me. What were you doing then that made it necessary to stay out the whole night and most of today? Darrell expected to be away only for one day.'

'I know. It was my fault. It was getting late and I suggested we should stay the night somewhere.'

'You must have been charmed with Darrell's company,' he drawled.

'Of course not! I mean, it wasn't that ... Darrell is very kind, but ...'

She had a sensation of panic as he came towards her and

If you were in their place what would you do?

Jeanette...

Though she has survived a heart-wrenching tragedy, is there more unhappiness in store for Jeanette? She is hopelessly in love with a man who is inaccessible to her. Her story will come alive in the pages of "Beyond the Sweet Waters" by Anne Hampson.

Laurel...

There was no turning back for Laurel. She was playing out a charade with the arrogant plantation owner, and the stakes were "love". It's all part of a thrilling romantic adventure called "Teachers Must Learn" by Nerina Hilliard.

Juliet...

Rather than let her father choose her husband, she ran...ran into the life of the haughty duke and his intriguing household on a Caribbean island. It's an intimate story that will stir you as you read "The Arrogant Duke" by Anne Mather.

Fern...

She tried to escape to a new life...a new world...now she was faced with a loveless marriage of convenience. How long could she wait for the love she so strongly craved to come to her... Live with Fern... love with Fern...in the exciting "Cap Flamingo" by Violet Winspear.

Jeanette, Juliet, Laurel, Fern...these are some of the memorable people who come alive in the pages of Harlequin Romance novels. And now, without leaving your home, you can share their most intimate moments!

It's the easiest and most convenient way to get every one of the exciting Harlequin Romance novels! And now with a home subscription plan you won't miss *any* of these true-to-life stories, and you don't even have to go out looking for them.

Get your
Harlequin Romance
Home Subscription NOW!

- Never miss a title!
- Get them first—straight from the presses!
- No additional costs for home delivery!
- These first 4 novels are yours FREE!

she felt his hard hands grasp her shoulders.

'Tell me, how could you bear to leave him after your night of love in the wilderness?'

She shook her head, feeling the bruising hands like eagle's talons on her tender skin.

'There was no night of love. How can you think so?'

'How can I not think so? You rejected me in favour of Darrell last night. You made it quite clear that he was the one who attracted you, even if your reactions to me were not exactly, shall we say, virginal.'

'That's a hideous thing to say! Let me go. I'm not answerable to you for whatever I do. I might have been once or at least, I would have been. But not now. Not any more.'

The black brows drew together in a puzzled frown.

'What are you saying? What are you implying?'

'Nothing, nothing at all.'

She had a sense of wild dismay. In the heat of the moment, infuriated by his enmity, she had said more than she intended.

'But why should you ever have been answerable to me for your actions? I don't understand. Why did you come here? Do you imagine I had some responsibility for you in the past?'

'If you had, it's over,' Perry replied bitterly.

He had loosed his hold a little, but he still kept her captive by that fierce golden stare and the scornful twist of the mobile mouth.

'I demand that you tell me whatever it is that you're hiding. It's obvious to me now that you haven't told me the truth, the real reason for your visit.'

'You've never given me a chance,' she explained.

This is it, thought Perry. I shall have to tell him now.

'I'm giving you a chance right this moment. If you're capable of being honest, tell me for what reason you came here, or am I making a mistake and it was just to renew your acquaintance with Darrell?'

She felt suddenly furious.

'Why do you keep harking back to Darrell?' she demanded. 'Leave him out of it. How many times must I tell you I have no interest in him? It's you I came to see. You're the reason why I made the journey. You're the reason why I went into the wilderness. But it didn't work.'

'What didn't work? What are you talking about?'

'I went to try to find out something, but I didn't succeed,' she explained.

'What was this something? I've had enough of your evasions. I demand to know what this is about.'

She drew a quivering breath.

'All right, I'll tell you. I went to find out whether I'd ever been legally married to you.'

Although she was terrified at the effect of her words, Perry felt a sense of immense relief. She had told him. Whatever happened now, she had told him the truth.

There was silence. A log shifted and crackled in the hearth. In the tree outside the window, a sleepy dove, settling in for the night, murmured to its mate, fluttered its feathers and then was quiet again. Somehow she had expected Tarquin to laugh her statement to scorn, but he appeared stunned. He released her from his grasp.

'Sit down,' he said, and he too sat facing her. 'I can't think I've heard you aright, but something must have led up to it. You must have a reason for making this incredible statement. You'd better explain.'

She was trembling violently, but she tried to speak calmly.

'When I came here before, five years ago, we went on a wilderness trail together. We started off with my grandparents and Darrell, but my grandmother became ill and my grandfather refused to leave her, so they went back with Darrell, leaving you and me to go on together.'

'I knew your grandparents, of course,' said Tarquin. 'I liked the old man immensely. But I have no recollection of your visit or of this wilderness trail. I have my doubts about the truth of your story so far. Why would they have left us to go on alone? Why didn't we all return?'

'They were very fond of me and they didn't want me to be disappointed. They thought of me as a child. They didn't think there was any harm in it.'

'And was there? Tell me more. I'm all ears.'

She realised now that his silence was one of disbelief, but she pressed on.

'We travelled in the wilderness for a few more days.'

'And what happened? Are you trying to tell me I seduced you?'

Perry winced, beginning to feel mentally flayed by the whips of his sarcastic tones, but there was no retreating. She must go on now.

'No, but we became attracted to each other.'

'Hardly improbable in the circumstances. So you were not such a child. I can imagine you must have been deliciously attractive at that age, very young and nubile. And you imply I withstood temptation. You make me sound like Sir Galahad—quite improbable. Definitely not me.'

She was determined now to keep calm and tell him the whole story, even though he obviously didn't believe a word she was saying.

'We came to a mission beyond the border of the reserve, and there . . .' she hesitated.

'Don't tell me, I'll tell you. I succumbed to the burning desire that I'd been enduring through all these tempting nights in the wilderness.'

'You married me,' she said. 'At least, I thought you did.'

'What in heaven's name do you mean, girl? Why on earth would I do that?'

'I thought it was because you loved me and wanted me for your wife, thought Perry, but she was silent, crushed by the bitter sarcasm of his tone.

'You arranged with the priest at the mission that there should be a marriage ceremony. I thought at the time it was valid.'

'You must be making this up. But why? How can this fantastic story possibly be of any benefit to you? Why did you come all the way to Africa to tell me this fable? Are you after money? What's the object of the exercise?'

'I told you, I want to find out whether the marriage was legal or not. At the time I thought it was, but later, when I didn't hear from you, I realised that perhaps it had just been an elaborate kind of hoax, an excuse to make love to me.'

'But what happened to break this so-called marriage? Let's hear the rest of the story. It becomes curiouser and curiouser.'

You asked me not to tell anyone and when we arrived back, I had to return to England in a hurry because of my aunt's illness. I wrote to you, but I never heard from you again.'

'You realise, of course, you're making me out a cad, a liar and a seducer of young girls?'

'I'm telling you the truth exactly as it happened. You must make your own judgment of your behaviour at that time. I made it five years ago, and let me tell you, Tarquin, nothing that's happened since I came here has changed it.'

He sprang up and started pacing up and down, then flung himself down beside her on the firelit cushions of the settee. Perry flinched at his overwhelming physical presence beside her and her nerves were as taut as violin strings as he took her chin in his hand, turning her face to look directly into his eyes.

'Look at me. That way I may know if you're lying. If this

fantastic story really happened and it's not a figment of an over-vivid imagination, how is it that I simply don't remember any of it at all, not even your face, which, in spite of all this rigmarole, I still find extraordinarily beautiful?'

'I didn't understand at first, but now I do partly. Darrell told me about your accident. It must have happened on the day I left, and the concussion made you forget everything about me. That's what I think must have happened.'

'Now you're accusing me of being mentally incompetent as well!'

Perry shook her head.

'Not that. But concussion does have strange effects sometimes. Darrell said you've forgotten quite a few things about your life before it happened.'

Tarquin frowned.

'So you've discussed me with Darrell? Do you mean to say that he also knows about all this?'

'No. Believe me, no one knows about it here. That's why I went with him, in order to go back to the mission.'

'You did? Well, now I'm beginning to think there's something to your story if you went to all that trouble to prove it. But I still think you made the most of your opportunities with Darrell too. So what happened? Did you prove you'd once been my happy bride?'

She tried to ignore his tone. Why does he seem to hate me now? she thought. He couldn't talk to me like this if he had a vestige of feeling left for me.

'The mission has been burned down,' she confessed. 'The records burned and the priest left.'

'Ah, I begin to see it now. All highly convenient. So now there's only your word to go by. Tell me, you say you're a journalist, and they notoriously have vivid imaginations, did you make this whole thing up only when you saw the burned mission?'

Perry gasped.

'You really are impossible! What would I do that for?'

'Oh, I don't know. It all comes back to money, probably. If you could make some claim on me however preposterous, it would make up for missing out on the personal interview you had intended to do in the first place.'

'Now it's you who are being fantastic,' Perry protested. 'How can you think I'd say I was married to someone as impossible as you if I didn't believe it? I don't want to be married to you—it's the last thing I want. The whole object of coming here was to prove it wasn't so. Will you please tell me how I'm to do that?'

'Simple. We'll find the priest and confront him with your story. Don't look alarmed. You've gone too far now to draw back. Even if the whole thing is a pack of lies, I feel the only thing to do with you is to prove it. This priest can't have married so many white couples in such a remote area. If he says he doesn't remember a thing about it, then I'll know you've been lying to me. Tell me, what was his name?'

'I ... I don't remember.'

'So. You should have got the finer points of your story a bit clearer before confronting me with it, shouldn't you?'

'Perhaps you could find out. Surely the African rangers might know his name.'

'Possibly. And where is this person living now?'

'Further north, near a lake.'

'Not very explicit. Do you know how many lakes there are in that part of the country?'

Perry shook her head miserably.

'However, as you suggest, maybe the rangers might provide a clue. I'll get on with my detective work first thing in the morning. Meanwhile I'll send Shadrac with your dinner to your room. Safer, don't you think? Far away from this wicked seducer of young girls. Tell me, just as a matter of interest, was this marriage properly consummated?'

Perry stood up and moved towards the door.

'That's one thing I'd rather not tell you. Perhaps one day you'll be able to remember.'

CHAPTER SEVEN

SHADRAC had only just brought in her breakfast tray next morning when Tarquin followed shortly afterwards. This time she felt his gaze upon her, not impersonal any more, but ... how could she describe the expression in those golden eyes? A little quizzical perhaps, and she wondered if he might be despising the pretty frilly negligee she was wearing.

'You won't have any use for that diaphanous garment where you're going,' he told her as if reading her thoughts. 'The priest who was at that mission was Father Mapamulo. I've found out more or less where he lives now, but it's some distance from here and it means you'll have to rough it quite a bit. After a while there are no roads, so we'll have to send the truck back and go on foot with donkeys taking any equipment we need with us, and we'll have to sleep rough. What do you say? Are you still eager to find him?'

'Certainly,' Perry told him. 'That's what I came for.'

'You don't want to withdraw your story and back down, saving us the trouble of a long hard journey?'

'Definitely not. If you aren't willing to go I'll get Darrell to take me.'

'Lorraine is very tolerant, but I hardly think she would appreciate your kidnapping her husband for a second time. No, if it has to be done, we'll go together. I must investigate your curious story myself.'

'Will there be anyone else travelling with us?' she asked.

'We'll take a couple of African rangers to help with the donkeys and supplies. Why? Are you feeling the need for a chaperon?'

Perry shook her head.

'No, not necessarily. I believe I can look after myself. I always have.'

'But according to your story you were not so successful the last time you ventured into the wilderness.'

Something smouldered in the gold of his eyes and she felt a flicker of fear, but she answered quite calmly.

'I was very young then and much too impressionable.'

'You're not exactly in your dotage yet.'

She felt her heart jolt as that golden gaze rested on her and she was breathlessly conscious of the transparency of the lacey frivolous garment, the way it seemed deliberately to reveal the soft creamy curves of her. She felt as self-conscious under his stare as she had felt long ago when she was little more than a schoolgirl.

'How long will the journey take?' she asked to cover her confusion.

He shrugged his shoulders.

'Who knows? The Africans were not entirely definite about the priest's whereabouts, but by asking as we go we should be able to find it in two days or so after we've left the road. Maybe less. Not as long as Stanley took finding Livingstone, I shouldn't wonder.'

'Will it be safe?' she asked.

'Not particularly. We'll be travelling on foot in an area where there are rhinos and lions as well as lesser beasts. Does that alarm you?'

'I suppose you and the Africans can cope with the conditions, otherwise you wouldn't suggest it. I have done a wilderness trail before, you know.'

'So you say. If you've done it once before you should know what to expect, but don't blame me if you find it tough going. According to your story, you'd just left school when you came here and so you were probably stronger than you are now. Certainly at the moment you don't look particularly athletic. I shouldn't think life in London fits you for the things you can expect to face in the next few days.'

'I'll risk it,' Perry told him.

'That's settled, then, I'll organise transport and so on today and we'll set out at crack of dawn tomorrow. Darrell keeps the stores at his place, so we'll go over there and stock up for the journey. By the way, I think we'll keep quiet about the real reason for it. Rather say that you want to do this expedition to try to get an article on wild life.'

He doesn't want Lorraine to know, thought Perry. Not for the first time she wondered what their relationship was. Later in the morning, sitting beside Tarquin in the Land Rover, she realised that Tarquin was driving her on the same path she had known five years ago, the road that led to her grandparents' farm. As she had suspected, this was where Darrell and Lorraine now lived.

'The first time we drove along this road and I came into the Reserve, we had a black-maned lion in the back of the truck,' she told Tarquin.

He looked at her incredulously.

'Now I'm sure you have to be joking!'

'You don't seem to believe anything I say, but it's true. You'd darted the lion. You came over to see my grandfather because it had broken through the fence on to his land, and my grandfather and I came to see you dart it with a tranquilliser.'

That was the first time she had met him. How vividly she remembered it! She could see herself now as she sat on the swing seat rocking gently, playing with a kitten. She could remember everything about it, the silky texture of the kitten's fur beneath her hand, the feel of the slip-on sandals half off her bare feet, the tingling bubbles of the lemonade she was sipping while she listened to the deep timbre of Tarquin's voice as he discussed the measures they were to take to capture the escaped lion. Every now and again she had glanced at his face and was sometimes aware that he was looking at her, though she could not interpret the expression in those mysterious gold-green eyes.

And later she had gone with them. She remembered as if it were yesterday the ride through the rough tracks, squeezed in the cab beside Tarquin, his strong brown hands swinging the wheel as he tried to avoid anthills. It was lovely then, she thought, the excitement, the thrill of being with him. The truck had been equipped with radio and he was able to communicate with the African rangers who had found the lion's spoor on a remote part of the farm. It had already killed a calf and they thought it would come back to the carcass later in the day. That part she hadn't liked, the smell of blood, the vultures waiting, bald-headed, horrible, watching from the trees, but she had tried to appear unmoved. She didn't want Tarquin to think of her as a weak English schoolgirl.

Now the sun had gone in a blaze of red and gold above the dark tops of the thorn trees and the creatures of the night were making themselves heard once more. A jackal ran across the clearing, pausing to dig with his nose for earthworms, then running on, slick and sure of himself. Deep in the trees a porcupine snuffled and grunted.

'It's time for some action,' Tarquin had said.

His hand brushed her bare legs as he reached across to the shelf in front of her, and she saw that he had a tape recorder which he now switched on. The darkening air was filled with the noises of the forest, hyenas shrieking and howling, baboons barking, then suddenly on the recorder they were silenced by the magnificent sound of a lion's hunting call echoing loud and free across the wilderness. Perry was bewildered by the sounds, not knowing which were real and which were taped. Then all at once she realised that Tarquin had switched it off and still the roar of the lion persisted. Below them in the direction of the trees there was a growling, tearing sound and, as Tarquin turned on a powerful searchlight, she almost screamed as she saw a huge lion with a dark ruff at the neck.

It was ripping chunks of meat from the carcass and, except for one lazy glance in their direction, it took not the slightest notice of the truck, all its interest being concentrated on its meal.

'Poor chap,' said Tarquin. 'It seems a pity to interrupt him.'

He opened the door of the cab. Perry pressed her hand against her mouth.

'I thought you said it wasn't dangerous,' she told her grandfather accusingly.

'For you and me, not for him,' he replied, his eyes on the huge beast. 'But don't worry, Perry. Tarquin knows what he's doing. It's all in a day's work to him.'

Now she saw that Tarquin was carrying a kind of gun and, as the lion turned to snarl at this man who dared to interrupt his meal, he let go the dart. It found its mark and the snarls became angrier. Obviously the beast was furious now at this disturbance. Tarquin stood his ground and in the circle of brilliant light, man and beast measured each other with gold-green eyes. It seemed to Perry as if Tarquin were actually willing the lion not to spring. To her it seemed as if their confrontation lasted for long minutes, but it was only seconds before the beast, with a long-drawn sigh, keeled over on its side.

Tarquin came back to the truck.

'That wasn't so difficult, was it?' he said. 'We'll leave him for a while until he's gone under properly. You won't mind having him in the back of the truck then, will you?

He'll be out cold for quite a while, but perhaps we should take him back into the Reserve before returning you to the farm.'

So the first time Perry came into Lion's Rock Reserve it had been with the prostrate body of a black-maned lion behind her in the truck. Driving through the wilderness, the darkness had seemed complete, but, beyond the path of the headlights, the night was full of secrets. Owls flew like gentle ghosts above the trees and from the side of the road a korhaan rose steeply skywards uttering shrill whistling cries. A chilly dawn wind had arisen, but Perry was only aware of the warmth of Tarquin's body pressed against her in the narrow confines of the cab.

This must all have passed through her mind in a flash, for she awoke from her dream to hear Tarquin saying, 'There were many times when I had to dart lions in those days, but I have no recollection of that particular time. Nowadays the Reserve is larger since we took in your grandfather's land and we've been able to strengthen the fences. We don't have so much trouble with straying beasts.'

I suppose it was all in the day's work to him, thought Perry. And it had been such a thrilling unique experience to her. Was that how it had all been to him?? Even those few enchanted days in the wilderness? An affair with a holiday visitor that was one of many?

It was an odd experience to see the old farmhouse again. The fences around the homestead had been made higher and more secure, but otherwise the place looked as she remembered it, with the great ropes of wisteria branches black against the white walls of the house and the pendant bunches of exquisite lilac flowers borne down by the frantic activities of the bees. But it seemed strange and all wrong when Lorraine came darting excitedly out like some highly coloured exotic bird and asked them into the house that was still furnished with Perry's grandmother's pastel chintzes. But where the rosewood piano had been there now stood a modern hi-fi set with large speakers, and Lorraine served them with iced drinks from a bar across one corner of the room.

'I see you still have the old curtains here,' said Perry with some pleasure.

Lorraine shrugged.

'Aren't they terrible? I'm longing for new ones, but we never seem to have any money to spare for them. I'd like something really bright. These are too wishy-washy for words.'

'I like them,' Perry told her, 'But then, you see, I have very happy memories of this place.'

'Oh, yes, you said you'd been here ages ago, didn't you?'

'I've decided to take Perry on a wilderness trail to-morrow,' Tarquin interrupted them. Did he think the trend of the conversation was getting dangerous?

'Really?' said Lorraine.

How lovely she looked, Perry thought, even in those tight bright orange stretch jeans and an exotically patterned brief top that revealed the whole of her body from curving waist to slender hipline. But her dark eyes were bright with anger as she caught Perry's gaze.

'The river won't be down for a few days and Perry wants to get photographs of wild life for a possible article when she gets back,' Tarquin explained.

'But can you spare the time?'

'It seems I'll have to,' said Tarquin. 'Darrell can deal with any emergencies while I'm away. He's extremely capable.'

'But why shouldn't Darrell take Perry?' Lorraine asked.

She certainly is tolerant, thought Perry, astonished.

'No,' said Tarquin. 'This is one duty I can't pass on to Darrell.'

Lorraine looked furious, but Tarquin did not seem to

notice, and just at that moment Darrell came into the room.

'The boys told me you want to see me to open up the stores,' he said.

'Yes, we need to stock up for a few days' travelling. You may as well stay with Lorraine, Perry. I take it you can put up with processed food for a couple of days? I'll choose the menu. I've done it often before.'

As soon as they were alone, Lorraine took a cigarette and paced up and down the room like a caged cat, but finally she sat down opposite Perry and stared at her with her fierce dark gaze.

'You're certainly taking a chance going off into the wilderness with Tarquin. How did you manage to persuade him to take you, and what would the boy-friend think?'

'It's more in the nature of a business agreement, Lorraine. Tarquin has consented to take me there to get photographs. There's no romantic interest, I assure you.'

Rather the reverse, Perry thought, since we're both setting out on this journey with the idea of finding out to what degree that ceremony bound us together and how we can break any ties there might be.

'I wouldn't be too sure,' Lorraine warned her. 'I've told you before, Tarquin can make use of any girl who shows she's willing, but I know him well. It doesn't really mean a thing to him.'

'Well, thank you for telling me, but I don't think your warning will be necessary as far as I'm concerned.'

'I suppose you think it will be romantic, but it's not at all comfortable camping out in the wilds. Life in the African bush is certainly not for me. I don't envy you.'

But she looked as if she did, thought Perry.

In the afternoon, Tarquin sent the two Africans on ahead with the donkeys. They were to meet them when the paths became too tough for vehicles, but Tarquin and

Perry were to do the first part of the journey by truck. Next day she was awake before dawn and showered quickly, then put on a blue denim slacks suit. The belted safari jacket was short-sleeved and the colour of her eyes, and with it she wore a checked blue and white sleeveless shirt. As she dressed she put aside the doubts about the wisdom of this journey with Tarquin. I have to know, she told herself, and this is the only way, but she hadn't bargained for the jolt of her heart and the tremulous feeling when she saw him waiting for her beside the truck.

The dark distant hills were taking on a shade of deep rose and there was a damp early morning smell of growing things as they drove off along the track that led into the wilderness. Glancing sideways, she could see Tarquin's strong brown hands on the wheel and his clear-cut features, the square jaw and the aquiline nose, and she remembered that other time five years ago when they had set out on this same road, but then she had been seventeen and she had worshipped him.

'The place towards which we're heading is by the side of the largest of the lakes, I believe,' Tarquin told her. 'It's almost like an inland sea, and impossible to see across to the other side. Well, at any rate, whatever the outcome of this crazy quest, you'll be seeing a part of Africa that many tourists would give a lot to visit. Just as well we decided to get on with this journey because this morning the rangers told me the river is going down. If there's no more rain, you'll be able to start your journey home by the end of this week. That should please you.'

'Oh, yes, it does,' said Perry.

But why, she asked herself, was she experiencing this sense of shock. When he had said she could go back home, it was as if she had suddenly collided with a blank wall that she had not seen before. But she wanted to go, didn't she? To get this over, to unravel the mystery of their strange marriage and then to go back to Sinclair, Sinclair with his deferential manner towards women, his well regulated way of life. Surely that was why she had come here, just so that she could return and get on with her own existence?

And never see Tarquin again? Of course, she told herself. She wanted nothing better than to lead a calm, ordered life, and that she could do with Sinclair, once all this muddle was disentangled. She had no desire to have the feelings that had troubled her during the last few days. The dubious attraction she felt towards this man at her side was merely an emotional remnant from that other time. He had been her first and only lover. No woman can forget the man who first possessed her body, no matter what she feels about him in later years.

But Tarquin? Had he really changed so much? Or wouldn't it be better if she faced facts and admitted that he had never loved her? Even now though he appeared to dislike her, he still found her physically attractive. Five years ago she had believed he loved her. But had she been wrong all the time? Had the accident had any consequences except to make him forget something that he really wanted to put out of his mind? Perhaps that was the explanation.

'I expect you'll be glad to get back to London. This place must seem pretty weird to someone who spends their life in a big city.'

'Weird?' said Perry. 'No, I wouldn't exactly say that.'

Weird? This brilliant sunshine, the startling blue of the unclouded sky, this wild lovely country with its tawny lion-coloured grass, flat-topped yellow-flowering thorn trees, strange shaped aloes, and its enchanting glimpses of animals, impala with glossy red pelts, giraffes startlingly tall with rocking-horse gait and huge film star eyes? No, it had a beauty that appealed to all her instincts, those senses that had been dulled by years of city living.

'It's my life,' said Tarquin. 'I could never lead any other

kind of existence, certainly not in town. But I dare say it couldn't possibly appeal to a girl who's been used to a more sophisticated way of living. You'll probably find it impossibly rough when we get out into the bush.'

'I think I can survive,' said Perry.

During the afternoon they arrived at the place from whence they had to proceed on foot. Two African rangers were standing by with donkeys and they helped to offload the equipment. They had food for three days' travelling and sleeping bags, but no tents, as Tarquin had cut their baggage down to basic necessities. They were each to carry a haversack and at once, over the small matter of adjusting the straps of this, Perry realised that this journey was not going to be easy. When Darrell had fastened her life jacket, her feelings had been utterly impersonal, but, when Tarquin was near her, adjusting the buckles with deft fingers, his bronzed face very close to hers, again she felt this tremulous reaction that she tried in vain to quell.

At last Tarquin judged that they were ready to proceed. Before them lay the wilderness, hundreds of bush-covered hills intersected by dark valleys where the curving river was a silver snake below.

'We'll follow the tracks that the Africans use. The bush is so thick in parts that it would be impossible even to take a horse along them, but the donkeys are surefooted and can pick their way through and around this kind of country,' Tarquin informed her.

It was early in the afternoon and the sun was still blazing down on the little procession as they started to wend their way along the winding track. Perry was glad when it led them into the thin shade of acacia trees. She could see that the Africans, one ahead leading a donkey and one behind them, seemed to be keeping a careful watch around them, and she could only surmise that they were keeping a lookout for wild animals which might be around. But in the drowsy heat of the afternoon, they were probably all sleeping. Oh, no, there in the dappled shade, hardly visible until your eyes became accustomed to them, were a herd of zebra grazing in the bush like live toy horses, fat little animals with striped coats accompanied as usual by a few wildebeeste, strange beasts with large fronts and noble Roman noses yet slim and seeming quite out of proportion in their back quarters.

Tarquin had provided her with boots, light Italian leather ones from the store that was once used by tourists. He had insisted on fastening them himself and seeing him kneeling at her feet Perry had resisted an absurd desire to touch that head of rough auburn curls. 'Comfortable?' he had asked, and had smiled when she declared they were marvellous.

'They'll be safe in case of snakes,' he had told her. 'Just keep a careful watch for those, but there's no need to be too petrified, because they're much more scared of you than you are of them. It's just a question of keeping a good lookout in case there happens to be one directly in your path.'

What had she let herself in for? she wondered, for certainly she was no athletic schoolgirl any more. She had been very much afraid that Tarquin would expect her to walk at a breakneck pace, but in this heat he did not seem to go fast.

'Normally I wouldn't walk at this time of day,' he told her, 'but we must get on if we're to make sufficient progress today. I'd like to reach a place where we can camp near water before sunset. However, I think you've been going long enough for a beginning. We'll rest for an hour and take some refreshment.'

A little way apart the Africans lit a fire and began to brew up some tea that they served to Tarquin and Perry in thick brown mugs. Around them the flat-topped trees seemed to quiver in the extreme heat. At first there seemed to be no sounds, and then Perry could hear the shrill chirping of insects in the grass and the sound of wood pigeons, mournful yet peaceful, rising out of the deep bush on the waves of shimmering air.

'Rest up for a while,' Tarquin advised when they had finished with the tea and eaten a couple of hard biscuits. They were sitting on a ground sheet and now he made her lie down, placing a cushion behind her head. High above the African sun blazed dazzling through the leaves and she was forced to close her eyes against the glare. She lay there listening to the lamenting sound of the doves and the yellow dry grass rustling in the wind, and after a few moments she was lulled to sleep.

She woke to the sight of Tarquin's bronzed face above her, the silky black-fringed eyes very close to hers. Those golden eyes seemed to be studying her face with great intensity. They were so near that she could see the dark pupils and his expression strange and mysterious.

'What is it?' she asked.

He shook his head and his eyes resumed their usual enigmatic stare.

'Nothing. I was wondering when you were going to wake. It's time to move on now if we're to reach our camping place before sunset.'

The heat of the sun had decreased as the day drew towards evening and now the animals had begun to move around, looking for water before they settled down for the night. On either side of them now there were furtive rustlings. Sometimes impala gazed at them in alarm and once a small grey duiker rushed across the path, then fled with a leaping jump into the bush.

All at once there was a shout from the African James who was leading the front donkey, '*Ubejane!*'

'He's seen a black rhino,' Tarquin told Perry. 'If it

heads this way climb up the nearest tree as quickly as you can.'

Perry wondered how she could possibly be expected to do this, since all the trees she could see were covered with thorns. Suddenly, as they came over a little hump in the ground, there it was, a weird-shaped black beast with a threatening horn and small malevolent eyes, not more than a few feet away.

'Stand still,' ordered Tarquin. 'We're upwind and it doesn't know we are here.'

His arm came around her shoulders as if to steady her and she was glad of its support, for she felt herself trembling and her heart beat wildly. Then she heard the African ranger in front of them shout, '*Hamba. . . . go!*' and waited scarcely daring to breathe and wondering what would happen next. But much to her relief the huge dark beast, after one startled stare at the donkey, wheeled around and trotted with remarkable agility across the grass and into the denser bush.

Tarquin's hand dropped from her shoulder, but she could still feel the bruising place where he had gripped her arm, and yet it had been reassuring at the time, she thought.

'Good thing he decided to go in the other direction. A black rhino is a most excitable, bad-tempered beast. If you'd ever seen a rhino charge you'd never forget it. There's nothing that can show more vicious hatred.'

'But it looks smaller than the white rhino. I saw some of those when I was with Darrell.'

'Yes, but the white rhino although it's bigger has a completely different temperament, you'll see.'

'Oh, will I?' said Perry. 'I don't mind seeing them when I'm in a truck, but I'm not particularly keen to meet them on foot!'

'You're hardly likely to travel through this part of the country without meeting some. Some years ago, they were almost extinct, but now they've been protected and have bred so well, there are almost too many. We're able to supply zoos all over the world. But, Perry, you mustn't worry about the animals we're likely to meet. It's all in a day's work and you're perfectly safe with me.'

And that's one of the unlikeliest statements of the year, thought Perry, as they finally came to the lovely glade where they were to make camp for the night. It was near to the river, where an enormous wild fig tree spread its roots over the ground and its branches made a perfect shelter for their camping equipment.

'There's a pool here enclosed by the rocks. You can bathe in there, but don't venture even into the shallow part of the river. There could easily be a crocodile lurking.'

As she splashed around in the shallow pool, that was reflecting the pink and gold of the sunset, Perry wondered how she could have this feeling of contentment when really there was nothing at all in her present situation to make her happy. It must be because I'm reminded of that former time, she thought, and in that lies the danger. I mustn't remember what happened before. I was young and too romantic. This journey into the wilderness is not for pleasure. It's the only way we can find out about the marriage, the only way I can feel really free of that bond with Tarquin.

A group of antelope were having a late drink beside the edge of the river as she came up the path and back to the welcome shelter of the fig tree. Already bats were wheeling around the sky in the half light and the Africans had lit lanterns to hang on the lower branches. One fire was blazing cheerfully, but the other had been allowed to die down to its embers already and here Tarquin was supervising the Africans as they heated a stew.

'I hope you're hungry,' he said. 'There seems enough here to feed an army.'

He seemed, she thought, to have become a somewhat

different person now that they were in the wilderness. He was not so hostile to her, and yet she did not know whether in the circumstances this was a good thing or a bad. The Africans, James and Jackson, had retired to their own fire a little distance away and she was left alone with Tarquin. Beyond the encircling glow of the fire, the darkness was alive with noise, shrill singing of crickets, the bell-like sounds of fruit bats, and, more sinister noises, the sound of genets growling and fighting like domestic cats, the cackling of a hyena, the mournful yip-yip of a jackal, the sudden alarmed yelp of a baboon.

Listening to these weird sounds, Perry found herself wondering again why she had chosen the hard way, why she had made this long journey to find herself on a wilderness trail with the man she had once loved and then had almost grown to hate. But did she hate him now? Her feelings were so mixed. She must be careful that the glamour of her surroundings did not make her feel attracted again to the man with whom she was sharing this adventure, for it was no adventure to him, no novelty to be out in the wilderness. This was his normal kind of living and he thought her story of their marriage was nonsense, but now she hoped very much that she could prove to him that that story was true.

'Are you scared, Perry?' Tarquin asked, seeing her start at some particularly wild cry from the bush.

'Certainly not,' she asserted stoutly. 'It's just that it all seems so strange.'

'The wilderness is really no place to bring a woman,' said Tarquin. 'In fact my whole way of life is not in any way attractive to the normal run of female. That's why I don't understand this mad idea of our having been married.'

'Don't let's discuss it now,' Perry implored.

'I've never even contemplated marriage,' he went on. 'The way I like to live is far too risky to take on the responsibility of a wife and family, and I'm sure I've always felt that way. How can you say that I could ever have come to the point of marrying a girl of seventeen?'.

'Maybe you didn't,' said Perry. 'But that's what we have to find out.'

'Certainly you're very beautiful, and I suppose you were already very attractive when, as you say, we met five years ago, but it's nonsense to even think of our being married now, don't you agree? Your life must be as different from mine as it's possible to imagine. Isn't that so?'

'Yes, I suppose it is,' Perry admitted.

But oh, Tarquin, she thought, when I see your face in the firelight, why do I want to lean forward and touch that curving mouth with my own?

A blood-curdling shriek followed by growling and sobbing wails came from the gloom and this time Perry could not help an exclamation of dismay. Tarquin put out his large hand and stroked her arm as if he were gentling some small, startled animal, but Perry did not know what dismayed her most, the dreadful sounds she was hearing or the thrilling sensations she felt at the gentle strength of his touch.

She listened to the sobbing screams of the pack of hyenas, but her mind was distracted from the terror of this wild noise by the sense of her own smooth skin under the touch of those bronzed fingers.

'There's no cause for alarm, Perry,' Tarquin said. 'They're far more interested in whatever food it is they're fighting over than in investigating our camp. Get into your sleeping bag now and try to rest. One or other of us will keep the fire going and stand guard during the night.'

He insisted that she should place her sleeping bag well inside the light of the fire and, when she was covered with only her head showing, he lightly touched her hair.

'Relax, Perry. You've had a hard day for a city girl, and

it's likely to be worse tomorrow.'

Every time Perry opened her eyes from her snatched attempts to sleep, she saw Tarquin, sitting there, his features dark and clear-cut against the rose-coloured glow of the fire. Every now and again he moved to put on another branch. What was he thinking of as he sat so still in the flickering hazy gold of the night? He was protecting her as ages ago primitive man had to protect his woman against the dangers of night in the wilderness, but she was not his woman, was she?

She thought fleetingly of Sinclair, but she could not imagine him in such surroundings. How far away her other life seemed. But what was she thinking of? That was her real life, not her other life. This was the life that was not real. It was only an interlude, and as a dream only lasted a few seconds so this would only last a brief few days. She looked up at the sky where a million stars swept the deep blue bowl of night and the Southern Cross swung high. Why do I still thrill to his touch when he's utterly indifferent to me? she thought, and then, for a little while, she slept.

CHAPTER EIGHT

At first light they were up and on their way. After her conversation with Tarquin yesterday, Perry was determined she must endure the rest of the journey with no sign of weakness, but it was very hard, more strenuous than the day before as Tarquin had truly predicted.

In the afternoon they came out of the wilder area and the country became more undulating with more signs of occupation. Sometimes they saw little groups of thatched huts upon the hillsides and cultivated lands around them. Now they were able to enquire exactly where the mission settlement was situated and towards evening at last they seemed to be reaching their destination.

On the horizon, the hills that had been sun-drenched and brown during the day were hazy and blue and against the blazing orange of the setting sun were silhouetted the black outlines of women who had been working in the fields, going homewards now with their burdens of sticks and pitchers of water. They sang as they walked and the sound carried clear in the evening breeze, monotonous, repetitive, and yet heartbreakingly sweet.

They were following an open path now and for some miles there had been tantalising glimpses of water, but now, as they rounded a curve in the path, the vast stretch of inland lake came into full view, so still, so peacefully blue, it was like a vision of heaven. Drifts of mist were rising over it, turning to pink in the glow of the setting sun, and pelicans and flamingoes as rosy as the clouds came in flocks to settle on the calm waters like so many giant flowers. On the grassy shore just below them there was a small group of round thatched huts painted white and a little church almost an exact replica of the one Perry had known before.

'We've evidently arrived at the right place,' said Tarquin. 'It will be best if you leave it to me to make the enquiries. I speak the language, and in any case I must be the one to ask Father Mapamulo for information. That is, of course, if he has any to give.'

'You can do the talking so long as I can be present at the meeting,' Perry told him.

How foolish she had been to imagine he had felt more kindly towards her on the journey! He had merely been carrying out the duty of protecting her, but now he seemed just as hostile as ever.

The bell on the steeple rang out suddenly, its sonorous clamour echoing across the still waters of the lake. Birds rose in clouds from the reeds on the edge of the shore and then settled once more, and from the small building came the sound of singing, a chorus of young voices, the tune sweetly harmonised, then the priest's voice raised in blessing. The doors burst open and a crowd of young Africans came out, the air about them resounding with excited chatter. They stared curiously at Tarquin and Perry and it seemed evident that they were not used to seeing white people.

'Father Mapamulo?' asked Tarquin, and they raised hands to point towards the church. They all wanted to run to tell him, but Tarquin indicated that they preferred to find him themselves. As they approached the church, Perry was assailed by doubt. She knew that Tarquin found it difficult to believe her story and she had hoped that the priest would be able to disentangle it, but suppose this was the wrong priest? Or suppose he too did not remember anything about it? After all, it had happened five years ago and all the records had been burned.

As they came into the church, Perry saw that the priest was standing with his back to them facing the altar. Was it the same one? And then he turned. As he stared at them, she thought, yes, it's him. I thought I might not recognise him, but I do. Everything about that time was so imprinted on my mind.

He came towards them—and then the miracle happened. He held out both hands and smiled, a smile that showed all his splendid white teeth.

'Why, Mr and Mrs Winslow, isn't it? What a very pleasant surprise!'

Perry looked at Tarquin and felt hysterical laughter bubbling up inside her. If she had wanted any revenge for his obvious disbelief of her whole story, she had it now.

'You recognise us?' asked Tarquin.

'Why, of course. It isn't every day I'm asked to perform the marriage ceremony as quickly as I was asked to perform yours. At the time I wondered whether I had done the right thing, but now I see you after five years, I can see you are still together and your wife is smiling, so I can tell that you are happy. Is good. Is excellent. Come now, we shall eat and afterwards we can talk and perhaps you will tell me something of your life together.'

He went in front of them and, as they followed him out of the church and across to his thatched house, Perry said to Tarquin, 'You said you wanted to do the talking. I'll leave you to it. I must say I'm very curious to know how you're going to deal with this.'

'Well, I must admit there must be more to your story than I thought at first. The old boy evidently thinks he married us, but I still have to be convinced that it really was a marriage. I'll deal with this in my own way.'

'But need you . . .?' she asked, and then she was silent.

'Need I what?'

'Need you let him know we're not still together? He seems so happy that the marriage he performed was a success. I'd hate to disillusion him.'

'Oh, good grief, you're far too sentimental! Why drag in his feelings? Things are complicated enough already. How do you think it feels for me to discover I have a wife that I didn't know existed and that I certainly don't need?'

'Hush!' begged Perry as the old priest turned around to usher them into the little house.

The brutality of Tarquin's statement had wiped away all the amusement she had felt at the priest's recognition of them. Why should she feel as if he had plunged a knife into a most tender part of her body? He was merely telling the truth. He didn't need her and she most certainly didn't need him, did she? They must find out whether according to law their marriage was legal, so if they had to pull down the old priest's illusions about their happiness, why worry, as Tarquin said.

But this, they soon discovered, was difficult. Father Mapamulo was so delighted with their company that he gave them little time for explanation. Over a frugal meal of vegetable soup, goat's cheese and corn bread, he talked about the fire at his other mission.

'You lost everything?' Tarquin asked.

'Unfortunately, yes. A Primus stove accidentally exploded. No one was hurt, but the buildings were tinder-dry after the long hot summer. We had little water in the rain tanks and everything was ablaze in seconds. All was burned, furniture, books, all my church records. We managed to drag out a little of the furniture, but not much. The office where I kept all my papers was right next to the kitchen and all my records were lost.'

'So actually you have no record of our marriage?' asked Tarquin.

Was he seeing this fact as a way of getting out of the complications? Perry wondered.

Father Mapamulo smiled.

'But most certainly there is. I have it right here, and now at last I can give it to you. I have kept it for five years hoping for just such an occasion as this.'

'What do you mean?' asked Tarquin.

His expression, Perry thought, was non-committal. She could not fathom what emotions were going on behind that inscrutable face, but they hardly looked joyful.

'Why, I should have given you a certificate of marriage when you were here, but when I marry Africans, they usually ask me to keep it for them and I overlooked yours. So I kept it safe, thinking that one day you would come back.'

'But how is it it wasn't burned with the others?'

Mr Mapamulo looked rather embarrassed, and put his hand in front of his mouth with a gesture of shyness.

'You are the only white pair I have ever married and I kept the certificate in my wallet. It was unusual, you understand, to have married a couple such as you. I was proud to have done such a thing.'

'But was it legal?' and as the old priest looked puzzled, 'I mean, was it according to the law of the land?'

'Oh, most certainly. Here I am allowed to marry quite young girls, sometimes in rather hurried circumstances, you understand. Is that what is worrying you? Is that why you came?'

Tarquin nodded. Perry thought his expression was rather grim.

'Something like that, yes.'

'Then you need no longer worry. According to our laws, the marriage was perfectly legal. Here is the certificate. I have kept it too long.'

The flimsy piece of paper was nearly falling to pieces

as he brought it out from a worn leather wallet, but in spidery writing and rather faded ink, their names and the date could still be seen quite clearly.

'I have talked too much about myself,' the old priest said. 'Tell me something of your life. How many children have you?'

Tarquin's expression relaxed into an ironical smile.

'No children as yet.'

'No? That is unfortunate. But your wife is very young,' said the old priest consolingly. 'There is time still.'

'Years and years,' Tarquin agreed.

'So that is another reason why you came here?'

'What do you mean?'

'You must have heard of the good reputation of my little church by the lake. Before there was a church even, this place had always been known to help the childless people. So that is why you have come, to pray together and to bathe in the waters?'

'It's as good a reason as any,' said Tarquin.

Perry looked at him quickly. Somehow they had got the information they needed from the priest without disillusioning him about their marriage, but really this was too much. How could Tarquin accept his reasoning that they had come here on some assumption that this place helped the childless? She frowned at him indignantly and he had the effrontery to laugh at her.

'My wife is embarrassed by this conversation,' he said. 'Let us hear more about you. Is everything going well with your mission?'

Father Mapamulo shook his head.

'Alas, no. We rebuilt the mission, as you see, and everything was going very well indeed, but now we have another problem.'

'Indeed, and what is that?'

'There is an elephant, *ndlovu*, he has been, how do you

say it, dismissed from his herd. He is old and sick and he is, we believe, in pain. He has some festering wounds and one tusk seems to be rotten. He raids the fruit trees and the crops on the outskirts of our village and lately, since the mopani trees have ripened, he has been eating their berries. When they drop to the ground, they go soft, and what is the word?'

'Ferment,' said Tarquin. 'An intoxicated elephant certainly would seem to be a tough proposition.'

'Yes, that is it. The berries make the beast drunk. Twice he has trampled our crops and if this goes on I do not know how we can stay here. We will have to start all over again in another place.'

'You're sure the elephant is very sick?'

'Oh, yes, Mr Winslow, he is very old too. It is time for him to die, but meanwhile my people suffer.'

His face, round and shining black, had been drawn into an unaccustomed frown, but strangely his expression became more cheerful and, with brilliant flashing white smile, he turned to Tarquin.

'But of course, that is why God has sent you to me at this time, Mr Winslow. It is an answer to my prayers. You are the man to solve our problem. You can shoot this great beast. It would be a kindness both to my people and to the animal itself.'

'But ... but that's impossible!' Perry stammered. 'It's madness to suggest such a thing!'

Neither of the men seemed to hear her.

'I'll certainly see what I can do for you,' said Tarquin. 'If I can get a look at the animal, I'll easily be able to confirm whether he's sick.'

'But you don't have a gun, do you?' asked Perry.

Oh, heavens, why did we ever come here? she was thinking frantically. She knew with absolute certainty that Tarquin would not hesitate to help Mr Mapamulo and his flock. Shooting a rogue elephant was an accepted part of his life, the life he had said no woman could share.

'Certainly I have a gun. I wouldn't travel in this part of the country without a high-velocity rifle. I didn't expect to have to use it, but there's always the chance the need might arise.'

Tarquin stood up.

'That's settled, then. I'll try to get a look at this beast in the morning. Come, my dear, we mustn't keep Father Mapamulo up beyond his bedtime. If he'll show us to his guest room, we can promise him to bathe in his miraculous waters some other time.'

Here then was another problem. Perry had not thought beyond the fact of meeting Father Mapamulo and hearing his story, but now she realised that they would be expected to spend the night here, and, since the old priest thought they were happily married, naturally they would be expected to share the same room. Reluctantly Perry got up from the table and slowly followed Tarquin and the African priest. A pathway led along the edge of the lake to a small thatched round hut made of adobe and whitewashed. There was just one room, bright with handwoven rugs and a gaily striped counterpane upon the one wide bed. Mr Mapamulo proudly showed them the tiny outside bathroom with its rather primitive shower and lavatory.

'Or if you prefer it,' he told them, 'there is a small pool right outside your window. We have dammed it, which makes it perfectly safe and free from crocodiles and hippos. A waterfall runs into it from the rocks, so it is always clean and fresh. You could even take a bathe in it tonight. The moon will be full.'

'Some other time,' said Tarquin. 'Does this pool have miraculous properties too?'

'That I do not know,' said the priest, smiling broadly. 'But its waters come from the lake. Good night, my child, sleep well. I will pray for you both tonight. The only thing that may disturb your sleep is the elephant. We will hope he does not choose to come here tonight.'

Perry waited until his footsteps died away, then she turned to Tarquin.

'How could you?' she demanded. 'How could you let him think we'd come here because we wanted a child?'

Tarquin shrugged.

'It was you who didn't want the man to be disillusioned on the subject of our married state. So what harm to seize on that reason for our visit?'

'It makes me feel ashamed. I wish now we'd said we'd been apart for years. That way at least he would have given us two rooms. I certainly have no intention of sharing this one with you.'

'No? So where am I supposed to sleep?'

'I don't care. Anywhere so long as it's not here.'

'Oh, for heaven's sake, Perry, stop being spinsterish!' snapped Tarquin. 'We've been together for two days in the wilderness and surely we have more serious things to discuss than arguing about who's to have the bed.'

'So you believe me now. You believe we're married?'

'I don't seem to have much choice. What a hell of a tangle! What's to be done? There must be ways of having a marriage like this one annulled.'

What other reaction did I expect? Perry asked herself. He's shocked and astounded and all he wants is to be rid of me. But how do I feel? All along she had told herself that the marriage would prove to have been illegal. She had thought that all she wanted was to find that out and to go back to her own ordered life and maybe eventually to consent to marry Sinclair, who would, she was sure, be a kind and generous husband. She had known ecstasy once in her lifetime and did not expect to experience it again.

But now that she knew the marriage had been legal and

that the vows she had made had been true, she found she had to rethink all her ideas. The bitterness she had felt was because she thought Tarquin had deliberately deceived her, and now she found he had not. Again she wondered how fate could have been so unkind to her. Tarquin had not led her into a false marriage just for his own gratification. He must have had some genuine feeling for her at that time, however transitory it had since proved. Now, after all these years, the whole position had changed. The accident had made him into a different person, short-tempered and seemingly incapable of any tender feeling, certainly towards herself.

He was shaking her shoulder, his fierce eyes frowning down on her.

'Come out of your trance, Perry. Did you hear what I said? There must be ways of having a marriage like ours annulled.'

She sighed.

'Yes, I suppose so.'

Is that what you want? she thought. Do I want it too? Of course I do. Isn't that why I came here? Be sensible, she told herself. He has no feeling for you at all or for the girl who became his wife when he was a different person. Not even a memory is left to him of that lovely time. At least I have that. Nothing can take it away from me now.

'You sound very noncommittal about it. Surely that's the whole reason why you came here, so you could find out about the legality of this union and if necessary have it annulled?'

He shook his head, and Perry thought he seemed like some fierce animal creature, a fighting bull tormented by spears.

'I still find it very hard to believe in this. How can I have forgotten anything as important as a marriage?'

'Perhaps because you wanted to forget,' Perry told him.

'And you ... why did you marry me? Was it a girlish infatuation that you've regretted ever since?'

How was it that in spite of everything he could still hurt her so badly?

'Something like that, I suppose,' she replied.

How could she admit to this arrogant man that she had thought she had loved him more than life itself?

'But why did you choose this particular moment in time to come back? It seems extraordinary that you should have left it for five years—or is there some particular reason? Tell me, is there someone waiting in the wings, hoping to pick up the pieces when we've dealt with this muddle?'

'What do you mean?' she faltered.

Perry knew very well what Tarquin meant, but she was playing for time. Since coming to Africa, the image of Sinclair had faded into the background and now she realised with dismay that, whatever Tarquin chose to do, that part of her life, the part she had shared with Sinclair, was over. While she had thought Tarquin had deceived her and led her into a false marriage, she could think about marrying another man, but now she had discovered that the marriage was genuine, she felt a strong reluctance to break those vows she had made so long ago in the little mission church. But this was nonsense. They had both changed. How could those few days they had spent together make her feel now that she could never marry anyone else? And yet they did.

'You know damned well what I mean. Is there someone back home whom you want to marry?'

Perry shook her head.

'No, not really. I admit I had considered it, but I'm not contemplating marriage now, not any more. But, Tarquin, whatever you choose to do, I won't stand in your way.'

He laughed sardonically.

'That's very big of you, Perry, I must say. It seems to

me that the sooner we straighten this tangle out the better. But why did you come here? Surely you didn't have some idea of remaining here as my wife?'

She wanted to lash out at him, to hurt him as much as he had hurt her.

'Certainly not! I wouldn't be married to you if you were the last man on earth!'

He had been standing silhouetted against the starry night beyond the small uncurtained window, but now he came over to her and, kneeling beside her as she sat on the bed, he took her face in his hands and looked into her eyes. His own eyes, gold flecked with green, in their dark fringe of lashes, were amused and enigmatic.

'But, Perry dear, you've forgotten something, surely, when you say that. You're married to me, my girl. I'm your husband whether you like it or not. Father Mapamulo says so, and, quite candidly, when I take a closer look at you, I'm beginning to enjoy the idea. Don't you think I should make the most of my opportunities just as I apparently did five years ago? That's a long time to be deprived of my wife, and after tonight, it might be another five years before I have the chance again.'

Perry felt a quiver of fear. His hands, so persuasive, were on her body now, and his chestnut head with its short, thick strong curls, was all she could see as he bent to kiss the creamy hollow where the buttons of the blue and white blouse met. Then she found herself flung back on the unyielding mattress, and, as he sought her mouth, the lithe strength of his body was upon her. She could feel the hardness of his thighs and the tremulous response in her own body. Her mouth parted under his and, feeling the savage insistence of his kisses, part of her wanted to let herself be swept away on this pulsating tide of sensuality that she knew had possessed them both, but she willed herself to resist and turned her head away from him, fighting him off until his hands eased their bruising grip and she lay beside him listening to his harsh breathing and her own light sighs as she struggled to regain her breath. He leaned over her and she closed her lids, afraid to meet the gaze of those wild golden eyes.

'Why are you resisting me? Surely you must once have been a very willing bride? Otherwise why should we be here?'

'That was a long time ago,' said Perry. 'And I don't even want to talk about it. We may still be married in law, but that's all, Tarquin. We're strangers now and I mean that we should remain so.'

'And as a stranger, you were more responsive to me the other evening than you are now. Why is that? Don't you trust yourself any more with me now that you know you're really my wife? You showed me before quite plainly that you were not really averse to my kisses, so why should you be now?'

Because you don't love me, thought Perry, because you want to use me only for your own gratification.

'Look, Tarquin,' she said now. 'It doesn't matter whether we're married or not as far as you're concerned, does it? If you were left alone in these circumstances with any presentable female, you would make the most of your opportunities, now wouldn't you?'

'Possibly, possibly,' said Tarquin, his white teeth flashing in that smile of mockery that she hated. 'But what about you? My wife was quick to make the most of her opportunities when she was left alone with Darrell, wasn't she?'

'You must know that isn't true! Darrell is a very honourable man. I was safe with him.'

'But you're not with me, is that it? But, Perry, as I've pointed out before, I am your lawful wedded husband and you've gone to all this trouble to find that out, so why not make the best of it ... for tonight at least?'

'What I've told you is true,' said Perry. 'I want nothing more to do with you. I've had enough. I wish to heaven I'd never come here and more especially that I'd never met you again. You only repel me now. Please leave me alone.'

She saw his expression change. The smiling mockery was expunged from his face as if she had slapped him. She turned her back to him to face the wall with its cream-coloured uneven plaster and buried her face in the lumpy pillow, that smelled of damp feathers. She closed her eyes and tried to breathe steadily and after a while she felt the bed creak as Tarquin moved away from it and she heard him walking softly towards the door, lifting the latch and going out into the night. Where was he going? I don't know and I don't care, she thought.

She was hot and tired and the scene with Tarquin had left her damp with perspiration. Should she have a shower? She got up and went to inspect the little cubicle that Father Mapamulo had shown so proudly. When she turned the tap, there was a faint trickle of tepid water that was a rusty brown in colour and there was an alarming groaning in the water pipes. Sighing, she went back to the bed and tried to rest again, but she did not feel she could undress and in the close little room she became hotter and hotter. A mosquito zoomed around her, its high-pitched whine seeming as loud as a jet plane in the stillness of the night.

Just outside the room, the night was very calm and quiet, the only sound the silvery splash of water just near by. What had Father Mapamulo said? That there was a safe pool just near the hut fed by a waterfall. Having at last disposed of the mosquito, she lay restless listening to the tinkle of the stream, like a crystal chandelier stirred by a cool breeze, and she began to long with a yearning desire to feel the splashing coldness of water upon her overheated, weary body. Where was Tarquin? He must by now have

found some other place in which to sleep. Maybe he had
gone back to the car, but she didn't care, did she? She had
made her point of view devastatingly clear to him, she
hoped, and she thought she need not fear a repetition of
the earlier scene.

I can't stand this hot stickiness a moment longer, she
thought. I have to do something about it. In the shower
room there was a large, rough, well-worn towel, and now
she got up, undressed and wrapped herself in it, then
quietly opened the stable type door of the hut and slipped
out. The moon was full, bathing the whole landscape in
luminous silver light. Beneath her bare feet, she could feel
the rough grass, delightfully cool and wet with dew.
Heavenly! she thought. In the moonlight, the sheen of the
still lake stretched into the distance and, near at hand, quite
close to the hut, a pool was caught like a pearl in its setting
of silvery boulders, a tiny miniature waterfall splashing
down into it like a decorative fountain. It was three o'clock
and the whole world seemed to be sleeping. Perry put aside
her towel and lowered herself cautiously down into the
tempting pool, feeling the carpet of soft sand sink beneath
her feet. Oh, this is paradise, she thought, this flowing coolness caressing her tired limbs. It seemed to sweep away all
the tautness, all the traumas of the long day. She felt
utterly relaxed, swimming with long strokes across the little
pool, her hair streaming out behind her like a mermaid's.

The moon was setting, yet it shone down on her, appearing not cold as it would have been in a northern clime, but
huge, pale gold and beneficent. She lost count of time as the
moonlit waters soothed her weary limbs, seeming almost to
restore her soul. She felt she could spend the whole of the
rest of the night here, idly floating on the opalescent pool,
splashed by the pearly drops of the silvery waterfall.

The noise of the falling water obscured all other sounds,
so she was not aware of an observer until she felt the

lightest touch upon her hand. It was as if a sea creature had brushed gently against her, caressing and tentative, but then she realised with a sense of shock that Tarquin was swimming beside her, his wet hair dark in the moonlight, his shoulders liquid bronze. She made a movement to escape from him, but he caught her by the shoulders and, as they sank beneath the surface of the silver pool, she found herself clinging desperately to him, feeling the hard maleness of his body against the curving softness of her own. As they surfaced, he drew her towards the side of the pool, where the waterfall splashed down among the ferns, and she felt his kisses upon her shoulders and the rainbow spray on her upturned face.

'Lovely one,' Tarquin whispered. 'Don't deny me. This night was made for us. Don't you feel it, don't you sense it?'

She felt her heart throbbing in slow terrible beats. Time had lost its meaning and she was overwhelmed by the dreamy bewildering sensations she had known as a young bride. To Perry it seemed that this man was not the harsh, arrogant creature that she knew now but the lover she remembered during the sad lost years, her dearest love who was carrying her over the dew-wet grass in the golden glow of the waning moon, to the little hut, cool now in the wind that blew before dawn. As he placed her on the bed, she felt herself drowning in the desire that throbbed between them and she knew that, when it came, her surrender to Tarquin would be like an exquisite kind of death.

Then suddenly, terribly, beyond the loud thud of their hearts, came a sound that she seemed to recognise from some other primaeval way of life—the awesome trumpeting of an angry elephant, followed by the screams of terrified people.

CHAPTER NINE

THERE was the sound of running footsteps and a quick tattoo on the door of the hut, then Mr Mapamulo's voice.

'Quickly, Mr Winslow, the elephant! It has broken down a store hut and killed two of our dogs!'

But Tarquin needed no summons. He was already dressing hastily and in a few moments was ready to go, having seized his gun from its hook on the wall.

'I'll come with you,' said Perry.

'Certainly not,' snapped Tarquin. 'You'll stay right here until I come back. I must get a look at this beast before deciding what to do.'

His expression was determined and preoccupied. Where now was the demanding lover of a few moments ago? It was as if she had dreamed it all. She heard the door creak as he bolted the bottom half of it, and then she was alone. She stretched out her arms, feeling on her soft skin the rough male kiss of the brown blanket that was her only covering, and she felt a sickening plunge into disappointment. But wasn't it all for the best? She had a shuddering sensation of panic when she remembered how totally she had been willing to abandon herself to his urgent desire.

What was happening out there? She dressed and went to the door. Tarquin had told her to stay here, but she felt worried and rebellious. Yet the moon was down now and in the darkness that came before dawn she could do no good stumbling around outside. She might even tread on a night adder. Far better to obey him, and yet how

138

could she endure this terrible not knowing? She opened the top of the stable type door and leaned out, peering into the darkness.

Away on the other side of the mission settlement there came a confused clamour of sound, followed again by the trumpeting roar that seemed to echo over the still waters of the lake and reverberate somewhere on the other side. There was a rendering crash followed by more screams and suddenly something, a thatched hut Perry thought, began to throw out brilliant sparks, spluttering at first like a fire-work and then suddenly alight. Against the background of leaping flames Perry could see tiny dark figures running it seemed in all directions, and there was something in the background, a dark bulk blacker than the night itself.

But now there was a new noise, a clattering of tins being beaten with metal objects, combined with the throbbing beat of drums, and as she listened to this ghastly mingling of sound, that dark shadow seemed to melt into the night.

She waited for a long time, peering out into the night. The flames of the hut died down so that all that was left was something that looked like the glowing heart of a huge red rose. The excited chattering of a crowd of people gradually died down and quietness descended upon the sleeping village once more, but still Tarquin did not return. Worn out with waiting, at last she went to lie down on the bed and although she had not thought it possible very soon she fell asleep.

She woke slowly, feeling completely bewildered to find herself in these surroundings, and on the small wooden table beside her bed she found a note. She was suddenly alert once more and her hand trembled as she unfolded the small piece of paper.

There was not even a formal endearment, merely a few lines scribbled hastily, 'The elephant needs to be destroyed. It's suffering and there's no cure for it. I couldn't kill it in the darkness, so I'm starting out straight away to follow its trail. I hope to be back before nightfall. I'm taking Jackson, my African ranger, with me but will leave James the other one, in case something goes wrong and you have to go back on your own. He's older, a very reliable chap, and can be trusted completely. Forget about last night. It was madness.'

Perry felt cold with fright and asked herself again why they had ever come here. She would rather a thousand times have been left in ignorance about their marriage than be assailed by this awful dread. Tarquin had lived all his life with danger, she knew. She thought of the way he had faced the lion when she had first met him, and with what casual nonchalance he had dismissed the episode of the crocodile, but this was different. An encounter with an angry sick elephant seemed to Perry to be the ultimate peak of danger. And what could she do to soothe the feeling of sick terror that had invaded her whole being?

She got up and faced again the inadequate shower, then dressed and went out into a glorious morning. The lake was a still expanse of shimmering milky blue with misty clouds lifting in the first rays of the radiant sun. On a tree covered with exotic red blossoms sat a large black and white kingfisher holding a small silver fish in its beak. Far out on the water a flock of pelicans rose in a white cloud, then settled down again upon the water like floating waterlilies. On such a morning surely nothing could go wrong, could it?

A young African girl came barefoot over the grass carrying a tray with an enamel mug of strong tea, a dish of corn porridge and a hunk of coarse brown bread.

'Lo blekfiss, ma'am,' she announced, smiling shyly.

'Mr Winslow ... when did he go?' asked Perry.

'Now, now,' said the girl.

This, Perry realised, could mean anything. It was a

phrase the African used to describe time but she thought it meant 'not so long ago'.

'Father Mapamulo say he come to see you after blek-fiss.'

Perry sat on a seat overlooking the calm lake and drank some of the strong tea and ate a little of the porridge. She crumbled most of the bread for the hungry gulls that were stalking around on the bank of the lake, looking at her with a cunning sideways glance of their small yellow eyes. Presently Father Mapamulo came hurrying across the grass from the direction of the church, the black skirts of his robe swinging as he walked.

'Ah, Mrs Winslow, so sorry you had such a disturbed night, but how brave your good husband was when the elephant came!'

'What happened?' asked Perry.

'Oh, this *ndlovu*, this great elephant was in a worse mood than any of us had ever known before. As I told your husband, it trampled one of the store huts, maybe trying to get at the grain, and then, when two dogs barked at it, it tossed them high upon its tusks. Poor creatures, they had no chance. But then your husband came and told my men to get saucepans and drums, but while he was organising this, the beast knocked against a hut and it caught alight because of the remains of a fire inside and thatch fell from the roof. However, thank God the people in the hut escaped. It would have been much worse if it hadn't been for your husband's help. He went inside the burning hut and dragged out the women and children who had been trapped there. They were too frightened and confused to know what to do. They had small burns, but not much. Your husband too.'

'Do you mean he was burned?' asked Perry anxiously.

'Not too much. Only his hands.'

'His hands? And he's gone out to try to shoot the elephant?'

Father Mapamulo laughed cheerfully.

'Ah, that one is *ndoda* ... a proper man if ever there was one. I put some medicine on his hands and wanted to bandage them, but he wouldn't have it. He said he would not be able to point the gun properly if I did that. He said it was nothing. They could be bandaged when he came back.'

'But, Father, isn't it very dangerous for him to go after this elephant with only one ranger with him?'

The little priest smiled at her fears.

'Not at all, my child, not to be worried. I have prayed for a long time about this thing. It will be quite safe, believe me. Mr Winslow was sent by God to help us. Of this I am sure.'

But I'm not sure, thought Perry. She was filled with horror at the idea of Tarquin being somewhere on the trail of that sick angry elephant with only a gun and an African ranger to help him and with hands that had been burned, to what extent she didn't even know. It was all very well for Mr Mapamulo to be so cheerful. Tarquin was not his loved one. Loved one? But was he hers? Oh, no, she must stop thinking this way. She had suffered enough when she was only seventeen. She must stop this foolish feeling that her emotions were the same as they had been then, for they were not. The difference was that then she had thought he loved her and now she knew he did not.

But how could she help worrying about the present situation? It would have been just the same, she tried to tell herself, if the man who had gone after the elephant had been Darrell. But would it? For Darrell she would have been desperately worried, of course, but she would not have had this feeling that if anything happened to him her own life might as well be at an end.

The long hours dragged past on leaden feet. How could he have left me like this? she thought ... to worry all day without one word of reassurance from him, and with despair she remembered the last words in the note, 'Forget about last night. It was madness.'

Maybe it was, Perry thought now, but if anything happens to Tarquin I shall always regret that I didn't have that night to remember.

Darkness came and still there was no word of him. Perry attended Evensong in the little church and heard Father Mapamulo praying for Tarquin's safety.

'He will come back safely, you will see,' the little priest told Perry, but he did not sound quite as confident as he had been this morning.

I must do something, Perry thought, and she went to find James, the old ranger who had been left behind.

'If they're not back by morning, could you follow their tracks into the bush?' she asked him, a wild idea beginning to form in her mind.

'Of course, *nkosikazi*, I can follow a trail very easily.'

'Could you take me there to wherever your master has gone?' she asked.

His brown impassive face, with the grizzled hair and short grey beard, showed little outward signs of emotion, neither disapproval nor surprise.

'But would the master wish it?' he asked her.

'I think he would wish you to go to him if he needs help,' she told him.

'But the master said I should guard you well.'

'You will guard me well, I know, but we will go together to find him. It's possible that he may have run into some trouble.'

'Yes, *nkosikazi*, it is true, he should have been back before nightfall.'

'So therefore we should set out to follow him at first light.'

'It shall be as you say, *nkosikazi*.'

While she ate a light evening meal at the priest's house,

Perry told him what she intended to do.

'I could send some of my young men after them into the bush,' he offered.

'No, I must go myself. I'll be perfectly all right. I'll have James to protect me. It would only slow things up if we took a big party.'

'Mr Winslow will probably be back before dawn,' Father Mapamulo assured her.

But he was not, and although Perry lay awake for hours she heard only the hooting of owls and the high-pitched yelps of the jackals, but no sound of the elephant that had terrified the village on the previous night.

At four o'clock, she got up and dressed in her toughest slacks, long-sleeved shirt, thick socks and the carefully laced Italian boots. She took care to dress in the beige-coloured garments that she had with her so that she would be inconspicuous, and she borrowed a khaki hat that Tarquin had left behind. The first glimmering light of day was shining mirror-like on the waters of the lake as James knocked on her door, and soon they were walking in the direction of the bush, going silently along a track still damp with dew. On either side of them there were signs that animals had been here before them and sometimes herds of impala looked up disturbed from their grazing.

James seemed to be noticing everything along the way, pointing out footprints in the soft sand, and then when the ground became harder away from the river, he was able to detect the other men's trail from small things like a broken twig or a crushed blade of grass. After a few miles they came to a clearing and James stopped, turning to Perry and saying the one word she had learned to know in the last few hours, 'Ndlovu.'

She was startled.

'You mean it was here, the elephant?'

'Yes, nkosikazi, just look.'

As she inspected the clearing more closely, it was very evident that the elephant had paused to feed. Probably frustrated by the turn of events at the village, it had uprooted young vegetation and stripped leaves from various trees. There were strips of bark upon the ground and white new patches where the beast had torn them off with his huge tusks.

'Now will be easy to find my master,' said James.

But the morning passed and afternoon came with its shimmering heat as they struggled along the trail of the huge elephant. It had cut a swathe through the bush that was for the most part visible, but the way that was presumably easy for an elephant's feet was not so simple for humans. The path was uneven and churned up, and branches of bushes alive with thorns whipped in to their faces as they tried to get along.

Presumably Tarquin and Jackson must have pressed on for the whole of the previous day, for they came across no signs of their having lit a fire, and, as the shadows started to lengthen, Perry began to doubt whether they could possibly catch up with the other two by nightfall. The bush seemed to be getting more and more impenetrable, and James had constantly to use his panga, a sharp curved knife, to cut aside the branches. Now it seemed to Perry that they had lost the path of the elephant, but James seemed certain that he was going the right way. Eventually the ground became a little more open and now they came to a glade of trees, but beyond that there seemed to be a tangled wilderness of acacias, marula trees and large wild fig trees.

'Rest here a little, *nkosikazi*,' James told her. 'I will go on to find the trail in those bushes over there.'

Perry sat down, grateful for a little respite from the long tiring journey, but with James gone she began to feel nervous. She had not expected to have to spend the night here in the bush and she tried not to think of the darkness that was fast approaching. Somewhere near by she could hear the 'Bom, Bom!' of baboons, their deep grunting coughs sounding as if something had disturbed them, and then she saw their dark shapes like a horrid caricature of dwarfed humans loping through the trees. They came nearer and a huge one, probably the leader, sat and gazed at her from a distance of little more than twenty yards. She remembered now that Tarquin had told her on the previous journey that baboons are much less afraid of women than they are of men and will approach women if they are left alone. Where was James? She began to wish desperately that he had not left her alone.

Then suddenly the baboons started to scream, high-pitched yells of alarm very different from the deep grunts she had heard before. The leader nearly tossed a somersault, so eager was he to get the others together and flee from the place. What could have disturbed them from their rather chilling inspection of herself?

She was soon to know, for suddenly there was the high shout of a man terrified out of his wits and the loud trumpeting of an angry elephant crashing around in the thicket that was a mere fifty yards away from where she was sitting. A shot rang out and there was a scream of animal pain louder than she could have imagined possible. Then the crashing noise became louder and it seemed to her that it was coming directly towards her where she sat frozen with horror underneath a flat-topped thorn tree. What had Tarquin said ... 'If you see a black rhino charging, you must climb a tree', and she had wondered how she could do it. Well, this was worse than a black rhino. It seemed to her that she must be directly in the path of the charging elephant.

Quickly she shinned up the tree, hindered by the smooth bark and yet scratched by the thorns upon every branch. But where was James? The crashing noise became even louder and with a shower of twigs, dust and leaves, the huge animal burst from the thicket. The tree where she sat seemed to shake as if it could be uprooted from the earth and the noise of the elephant's feet pounding upon the ground sounded to Perry like thunder. Level with the branches to which she clung, she could see the great flapping grey ears, the wrinkled back of the huge pachyderm. For a few seconds that seemed to freeze into hours as she sat, she saw the elephant's small mean eyes and was sure that they looked directly into her own. But they had not seen her. She saw the great lumbering back of the beast with its heaving flanks and thin ludicrous tail disappear into the bush from whence they had themselves emerged only a little while ago. It had gone, but where it had passed there were broken branches and upon the white new wood were drops of bright red blood.

And now in the sudden quiet she could hear voices, and it seemed to her that one of them was raised in anger. Oh, yes, she knew that voice. She slid down the trunk of the tree, feeling her way from branch to branch much more slowly than she had shinned up. The feeling of relief when she had recognised Tarquin's voice was mingled with dread. Slowly she walked forward in the direction of the sounds.

'Perry, what the hell are you doing here?'

The surge of joy she had felt as she saw his lithe frame moving towards her was quenched by the look in his eyes that were fierce and golden as a falcon's. But still she wanted to run towards him, to bury her head on that strong chest just above the beat of his heart, and to tell him, 'I had to come. I couldn't bear it any longer.'

'You didn't come back!' she exclaimed. 'They said your hands were burned. I was afraid something had happened. I thought I'd better bring James and come in search of you.'

Something, she didn't know what, flickered in his eyes.

The hardness seemed to soften a little or had she imagined this?

'It was very foolish of you,' he told her. 'You look as if you've had a hard passage.'

She looked down, seeing herself through his eyes now, the tangled hair full of twigs and leaves, her shirt torn on the shoulder where the thorns had ripped it, her scratched arms, the boots and slacks covered thickly with dust, but she was not aware of the dark blue shadows under her eyes, the paleness of her face beneath the even gold tan.

'But even Father Mapamulo said you should have been back before nightfall,' she protested. 'I imagined you lying somewhere with a broken leg or worse.'

'Then you have a good imagination. No, Perry, hunting an elephant in the bush, especially one as old and wily as this one, is not child's play. It takes time, and now, thanks to you and James here, it's going to take more time.'

'What do you mean?' she asked.

'We trailed the elephant for the whole of yesterday and gradually we started to gain on it. Finally it rested up in this thicket for the night. I thought it would come out of there with the dawn, but, as I told you, it's a cunning old beast. Whether it got a whiff of our scent I don't know, but it seems likely, so it stayed concealed for the whole day. I couldn't hope to get a good shot at it in such thick bush, so we waited and waited, hoping that with evening coming on it would have to move because it would need to search for water.'

It was amazing, thought Perry, that Tarquin, so impatient in little things, could wait patiently in this place for the whole of one day.

'It was just showing signs of starting to move out, when James here disturbed it. It came out sure enough, but, as you saw, it came out at a gallop. I had thought that if it had been moving slowly, not aware of any man at hand, it would have been easy to finish it off with a shot, but James, and I don't really blame him in the circumstances, panicked and used his gun, which is a simple rifle, quite unsuitable for a large beast like this one. I heard the pandemonium but couldn't get near enough to get a shot. So now the game has to start all over again, but this time the elephant is wounded and you're here.'

'What are you going to do?' asked Perry, trying to ignore the feeling that by her actions she had made the situation much more difficult and dangerous for Tarquin.

'Spend the night here, what else? We'll keep watch, but probably the elephant will stay holed up in the other thicket, specially as he's wounded. At first light I'll send James back with you and we'll continue our vigil. It's just going to be a little longer and more dangerous now, but it can't be helped.'

'You can't send me back now,' Perry protested. 'Please let me stay. I can't stand not knowing what's happening. I'd much rather be here.'

Tarquin sighed wearily. The bright bronze of his hair was eclipsed by sandy dust and his safari jacket clung wrinkled to his large frame.

'I've told you before, girl, Africa is not suitable for Sunday School picnics. There's a wounded, sick, angry elephant in that bush just biding his time to get his own back on man, whom he regards now as his enemy. This is no place for any woman, much less one who's spent most of her life in a city.'

Perry thought it was no use to keep on arguing, but she was determined that when the time came she would do her utmost to stay with Tarquin. Jackson and James had been sent to reconnoitre and came back with the news that, as they had surmised, the elephant was hiding in the thicket some way from the clearing. It was almost dark now and clearly it was no use pursuing the hunt. The two Africans lit a fire and warmed the tins of stew that Perry had brought with her.

'That was one good idea you had,' said Tarquin when they had finished.

'The only one, do you mean?'

'Maybe. You can take it as you like. I can tell you this, it was a very astonishing sight when you suddenly appeared.'

Very unwelcome too, thought Perry. But I'd rather be here with this dangerous animal only a few hundred yards away and Tarquin beside me than way back there at the lake with the worry of not knowing what's going on.

She shivered a little.

'Are you cold?' asked Tarquin. 'Here, take my jacket.'

He stripped off the safari suit and put it around her shoulders. In the firelight, his chest was a reddish bronze shadowed by the silky pelt of curling dark hairs. Perry remembered how she had caressed those smooth pectoral muscles as they had embraced in the shining coolness of the water only last night, but it seemed a world away.

Moonlight flooded the clearing and huge stars like yellow daffodils seemed much closer to earth than they ever did in more northern countries.

'How are your hands?' she asked.

'Almost better. Who told you about that?'

'Father Mapamulo.'

'He talks too much. I told him to keep quiet about it.'

'Let me see them.'

Reluctantly he put out his hands and taking them gently one by one Perry shone her torch upon them. The palms looked fiery red.

'They should be bandaged,' she said, 'Or you should have gloves for them.'

'Gloves!' Tarquin laughed with genuine amusement. 'Where would I find gloves? I've never worn such a thing in my life.'

She felt a few tears run down her cheeks and on to the hands she was holding so carefully and she waited for some scathing remark about women who weep, but he took a handkerchief from his top pocket and without comment wiped her face dry.

'By anyone's standards you've had a difficult day, Perry. Now you'd better try to get some sleep, and I'll snatch a little rest too. James and Jackson have instructions to wake me if anything happens. They'll keep watch for an hour or so, then I'll take my turn.'

She lay down upon the groundsheet and he covered her with the jacket.

'Won't you be cold?' she asked.

'Not to worry. I'm used to any temperature, hot or cold,' he assured her.

He lay down too on the far end of the groundsheet and turned his back to her. She lay there looking at the stars and her thoughts wandered to the night before. How different this Tarquin was from the lover she had known for that short time. Or had she imagined it all? She looked at his back, bulky in the moonlight, and she longed to touch his shoulder and somehow make him look at her with an expression in those golden eyes that was not indifferent and cool but warm with desire. But she did not dare. At last, lulled by the rustle of the leaves in the nearby mopani trees, she fell asleep.

She slept, but all the time aware that she was restless and not warm enough. She heard small noises and then, still half asleep, she felt Tarquin's hands that were soothing her as if she had been a wakeful child and she knew that the whimpering sounds had been her own.

'Sleep now, Perry. There's nothing to worry about. The elephant won't move before daylight.'

She felt his arm slip around her and his other hand turn her head to rest on his shoulder that was bare and warm and comforting, and then she slipped into a deeper sleep that was untroubled by dreams.

She woke suddenly knowing that some noise had roused her. A grey light was filtering through the trees, and then she heard it again, the now familiar high trumpeting, the sign that the elephant was stirring into some new action. It was some distance away and yet it sounded so loud that it could have been just outside the clearing.

'It's too late now for you to go back. Stay here, and don't do anything foolish while we're away,' said Tarquin.

He was buttoning the discarded safari jacket and was reaching for the gun that had been beside him all night.

'If it shows signs of heading this way we'll shout and you must go up in the tree as you did before. But I hope to get it as soon as it decides to come out in the open.'

But even as he spoke, James and Jackson came rushing towards him.

'*Ndlovu*, it's come out of the bush and is heading this way!'

Perry felt herself being swung up and lifted towards the lower branches of the great tree.

'Get up higher and stay right there,' Tarquin told her.

He picked up his discarded gun and strode off in the direction of the now terrifying sounds of a large beast crashing through the bushes, but as he reached the edge of the clearing the whole landscape seemed to erupt like a volcano. The enormous animal came bellowing out of the thicket, scattering branches of trees in its wake. It seemed to see the two Africans first and advanced towards them as if to brush them aside like a cow getting rid of troublesome flies. But with that Tarquin shouted and it turned towards him. Perry pressed her fist tight into her mouth to prevent the scream that wanted to come piercingly from her throat as she realised that she had never experienced terror like this in the whole of her life, but she dared not make a sound.

She had done enough damage with her interference in Tarquin's plans.

She could see the great red throat of the animal, a gaping cavern between the long old yellowed tusks and the trunk that was raised in rampant anger. A few more yards and Tarquin was bound to be trampled under those feet that were the size of the boles of great trees. She saw him stand his ground, then calmly raise the gun to shoulder height. There was a shot and then another. The beast stopped in its tracks, hesitated and then with the thunderous crash of a felled tree, it collapsed, legs floundering, its huge ears drooping pathetically as it breathed its last. Small sapling trees had been uprooted and the air was filled with a cloud of dust and leaves.

'Stay where you are!' shouted Tarquin, and strode across to the huge carcass. And then after what seemed hours: 'It's all right, it's properly dead.'

Perry slid down the tree again and into his arms where he waited underneath to help her down. She found that she was sobbing and clinging to him as if she would never let him go.

'Good grief, girl, stop it, do! I'll be drowned if you keep on like this. It's all over now. A great pity I had to shoot that poor beast.'

She noticed that he hadn't told her he couldn't stand a woman who wept, as he had told her twice before. Well, she must be thankful for small mercies, she supposed.

But now she knew. Now all her doubts were gone. She had realised in those moments when his life had been in the balance that she loved Tarquin just as much as she had when she was a young bride all those years ago. No, not just as much, but even more, with a mature love that she did not know how she was going to bear.

CHAPTER TEN

THEY were going home by a different route that Tarquin had heard was shorter, and all day they travelled through the wilderness, going away from the mission where they had left Father Mapamulo and his flock rejoicing. At first the water stayed with them beside the track and large fever trees with bright green barks grew along its reed-covered banks and the pools were dotted with waterlilies. Spur-wing geese swam upon the water and purple gallinules trotted upon the lily leaves. Further on, upon the slopes, aloes grew in profusion and fossilised trees could be seen, prehistoric giants brought down like Goliath.

They made good progress and in the afternoon arrived at the truck and parted from the Africans who were to follow with the donkeys. Tarquin was silent, seeming to concentrate on his driving upon the rough road, and Perry watched the changing landscape, the open glades with dark flat-topped thorn trees that seemed to quiver with waves of heat. Sometimes zebra and wildebeeste kicked up their heels at the sight of the truck and galloped away, and warthogs ran with uplifted tails, their young following them in ludicrous procession. Why was she seeing all this in such a daze of misery, she wondered, when at another time it would have made her so happy?

Why am I doomed to love a man like Tarquin? she thought. We're completely unsuited and he's told me himself that he can never share his life with a woman like me.

They had hoped to make swift progress, but when evening came they were still far from their destination.

'We aren't going to make it, I'm afraid, Perry, but at least we don't have to spend another night outdoors. We can stay at the place where you and Darrell spent the night.'

Perry shuddered. It was the last thing she wanted to do to spend the night with Tarquin in the intimate surroundings of the little hut.

'Oh, no, Tarquin, we can't! I don't want to.'

Tarquin shrugged as if he could not understand why she should object. He had stopped the truck and around them was the hum of cicadas and the crackling sound of grasshoppers.

'What's wrong? Do you have sweeter memories of the night with Darrell than you expect to have with me?'

'Of course not. Don't be absurd! I've told you before that night with Darrell was perfectly innocent.'

'Have it your own way,' shrugged Tarquin.

He doesn't believe me, thought Perry. Does he think then after last night that I would behave so with any man? It seems like it. But how can I make it right? There's no way to convince him without telling him the truth, that I love him, and I can't do that. He would destroy me with his laughter.

'Even if we reached home, we would still be spending the night unchaperoned, so what's your objection to another night in the wilderness?' asked Tarquin. 'As you agreed, Perry, what happened or nearly happened two nights ago was crazy, utterly foolish. It was fortunate indeed that we were interrupted. I can promise you it won't happen again.'

How could he sound so certain? She herself wished desperately that they could have managed to get back to the house with its long passages and rooms remote from each other instead of having to spend the night in the close confines of the little hut. She did not trust Tarquin, and worse, she didn't even trust herself.

She tried not to think about it as they lit the wood fire, warmed the soup that had been left there for emergencies and cooked the contents of a tin of sausages over the embers. Tarquin piled logs on to the fire again and they sat in front of it on the shabby rug, holding mugs of strong black coffee. Tonight he had not even touched her hand, but if he tried to make love to her again, what would she do?

Outside the sound of a hundred tree frogs made one shrill pulsating sound like the beat of her own heart, and within the little hut there was firelight dancing on the white walls and the wooden beams and the dark thatch, emphasising the living bronze of Tarquin's rugged features and the sensuous curves of his mobile mouth. If I could stay with him, Perry thought, if I could only stay here beside him, I wouldn't ask for more. Even if he only used me, as he tried to do the other night, it would be better than going back to a life that's become completely without meaning.

Seated on a cushion beside the flickering flames, she could see a pulse beating in his throat where the dark tendrils of hair curled away from the open neck of his shirt, and she had an insane desire to press her lips upon that place and to reach upwards to that curving mouth and feel the cruelty of his kisses upon her own tender skin.

Stirred unbearably by the wanton nature of her thoughts, she had a violent impulse to go to him and tell him that she would never leave him, that, if he desired her in any way, she would stay here and they need never part. But what would be the use? He had stated quite emphatically that all he wanted was to be free of her. She could not risk further humiliation.

There were rough bunk beds on either side of the fireplace and, after a while, they rolled themselves in the brown blankets and tried to settle themselves to sleep.

Perry lay awake, seeing the light of the flames flicker in streaks of gold over the white walls, then gradually die down to a steady rosy glow. Some time later she heard Tarquin stir and say, 'Perry, are you still awake?'

'Yes,' she said, her heart throbbing wildly.

'Can I be certain that what you said is true and that there's no one waiting in the wings to pick up the pieces?'

She thought of Sinclair, but it seemed to her as if that had all taken place in a previous part of her existence and now he was of no importance in her life any more.

'There's no one, Tarquin,' she said.

Why had he asked this question? She waited in the darkness, hardly daring to breathe, half expecting that he would come to her, and, when he did not, she felt weak with disappointment. But how can I feel like that about a man who seems to despise me? she thought.

Driving back next day, she thought, it's finished now. It's all over. It would have been far better if I'd never come back, then I would never have had to suffer this cruel heartbreak all over again. Last time I was a girl, but now I'm a woman and the grief seems much harder to bear. What possessed me to think he loved me that night at the lake? She trembled when she thought how that night she had been willing to surrender her body to Tarquin with such passionate abandon. And now this same man she thought she loved was sitting at her side, and it seemed to her that he had an iron heart that could never be moved to any tender feeling.

'I told Darrell to try to book you on tomorrow's plane if the river has gone down today,' Tarquin informed her.

How dreadfully eager he is to get rid of me, she thought.

'We should start proceedings as soon as you get back. The sooner we get it over with the better. It will probably be better if I see to it, since we were married in this country. You can let my lawyer know the details later,' Tarquin told her.

'Just as you please,' said Perry, trying to sound indifferent.

'And, by the way, nobody need know we've been together again during the last few days. Might make things awkward, don't you agree?'

'I suppose so,' said Perry.

'The best thing that can happen is that we should both forget about these last few days. Let's pretend it never happened. We're both agreed that what almost happened the other night was madness. Right?'

'Certainly I don't want to remember it. I'd rather put it right out of my mind.'

'Was it so distasteful to you, then?' he drawled.

'You must draw your own conclusions. It's not a thing that I wish to discuss any more.'

'You're very diplomatic. If you'd said you'd hated what passed between us that night, I wouldn't have believed you. You have a very sensual nature, Perry. Some day you'll make someone a very exciting wife.'

But I'm your wife, she wanted to cry out. I'm sensual only for you.

'I have no intention of marrying again,' she told him.

'But you want to be free.'

'Naturally.'

But did she? Yes, of course. She wanted to be free of this whole sorry tangle. The sooner she could get away from Tarquin's proximity, the better she would be pleased. He had tried to use her for his own satisfaction and now he was throwing her aside. How could she imagine she could be attracted to a man like that? And yet she was. While they talked calmly of their separation, she was imagining an impossible dream, that he would suddenly say, 'This is all nonsense. Don't you know I love you?' and take her in his arms again.

She tried to keep her eyes rigidly upon the road ahead,

but found herself irresistibly drawn to the sight of his long lean brown hands on the wheel, the rippling bronze muscles of his chest under the open khaki jacket, the steely strength of his thighs beneath the tight corded jeans. How can I go away tomorrow and never see him again? she thought.

She would be glad to get back to the house. There she would occupy herself in packing her few possessions, then perhaps Shadrac would serve dinner in her room and tomorrow she would be on her way. She longed desperately to be alone with her thoughts.

But as the vehicle stopped in the driveway in front of the pillared portico, Lorraine hurried towards them.

'Surprise, surprise!' she cried, almost before they had descended from the truck. She was smiling vivaciously. Perry, who had thought Lorraine might be most annoyed that she had stayed away with Tarquin longer than they had intended, was quite astonished that she should be so pleased with life. She was looking very attractive in a chalk white sundress that emphasised her dark beauty and her even tan, the deep plunging top showing her lovely back and the creamy curves of her breasts.

'You're going to be very thrilled when you know who has arrived to fetch you,' she told Perry.

A figure was rising from the white wrought iron seat on the patio, a man in a cream shantung suit, beautifully cut, very suitable for the tropical heat and yet appearing totally wrong in the setting of the wilderness, where the usual garb was tough khaki shorts and safari jackets. Sinclair! Perry had never expected to see him here. He took her hot hands in his cool ones and kissed her lightly.

'Perdita, my dear! It's good to see you.'

'But ... but, Sinclair, what are you doing here?' she stammered.

'I found I had to fly out on some business, so I decided to come and fetch you. You've been away from London for longer than you promised, but now I hear you're to go back tomorrow. That's most fortunate. It means we can travel together which is what I hoped when I came here.'

'You two must have a lot to say to each other. Let's leave them alone, Tarquin. We'd better go inside. Isn't it romantic that Sinclair came all this way to fetch Perry home? That's what I call true love. Come along, Tarquin. I'm sure they want to be by themselves. I've been arranging a special dinner with Shadrac for tonight. I thought that would be what you wanted since Perry's leaving tomorrow.'

Confused and bewildered by Sinclair's unexpected arrival and now Lorraine's babbling, Perry stole a glance at Tarquin. His face was still, set in a rigid expression like a wooden image, his golden animal eyes cold with fury.

'Certainly Perry must have a lot to tell her visitor. I wonder what she'll have to tell him about her journey into the wilderness. Not enough to alarm him, I hope.'

He followed Lorraine into the house and, as Perry watched the dark lovely woman clinging to Tarquin's arm, she turned to Sinclair wondering what on earth she could say to him.

'So that's Tarquin. He looks a surly brute,' was Sinclair's first comment. It was pretty evident that both men had taken an instant dislike to each other.

'He's changed. He's not like he used to be. He had an accident,' Perry told him, and she explained what she had found out.

'So. You're not free, it appears, and you will have to go to all the trouble of legal action to dissolve this farce of a marriage.'

How had she ever thought of Sinclair as a possible husband? Perry wondered. She found herself disliking his prim appearance, his look of distaste as he spoke of the need for legal action. But how could she blame him? She hated the idea herself.

'I presume he's willing to give you your freedom?' Sinclair added.

'Oh, certainly. He can't wait to go through with it. It was a great shock to his system to find that he was married to me,' said Perry bitterly.

'This woman, Lorraine, seems very possessive with him. Is there anything in that?'

'I don't know. She's always seemed to be attracted to him.'

'And he to her, I shouldn't wonder. Well, that may make it easier for you.'

'In what way?'

'If he wants his freedom in order to marry her, he won't delay the proceedings.'

'No, I suppose not,' Perry agreed.

How could she feel so hurt at what was only a plain fact for anyone to see?

'What's his attitude to you now? Was he attracted to you you again?'

'He seems to dislike me.'

How could she tell Sinclair about the events of the last few days? It could not make any difference now she had made up her mind that she could never marry him. But she could not tell him that now. It must wait until they were back in London.

'I should never have left you to come here on your own. Heaven knows what might have happened to you again with such a man.'

From the rocks near by came the screams of a trumpeter hornbill, brassy and wild, making the cliffs echo to the sound.

Sinclair shuddered.

'What a country,' he said. 'Even the birds sound uncivilised. I'll be glad when we can get away from here tomorrow.'

'So shall I,' said Perry, but she knew it was for a different reason.

She was glad when she could leave Sinclair with the excuse that she really did need to bath and change before dinner. After the rather basic conditions she had experienced in the wilderness, it was heavenly to slip into the warm scented bath and then put on lacy cream undies and a light voile dress patterned in cool shades of turquoise and lilac. She brushed her newly washed hair until it shone like golden Chinese silk, and, carefully sweeping up her curling dark lashes, she coloured her lids with a shade of Aegean blue. She was just applying a rose-coloured lipstick when there was a light knock on her door and there stood Lorraine, smiling very amiably.

'Perry, how nice you look! But there, I suppose this is all in honour of Sinclair. I came to tell you how very happy I am for you. I'm so glad you have someone to turn to. It's such a horrible situation for you and Tarquin and the sooner you can do something about it the better.'

'You know about it?' said Perry, somewhat astounded.

'Yes, of course, my dear, and Sinclair agrees with me that for all our sakes the legal side must be done quietly and quickly.'

'For all our sakes? What exactly do you mean by that, Lorraine?'

Perry was surprised and bewildered that Lorraine had got to know about their marriage so quickly. It meant that Tarquin must have told her as soon as they were alone together. Perry felt let down by this. But what loyalty could she expect from Tarquin? He was a stranger to her and Lorraine was his intimate friend.

'I mean that as soon as Tarquin has got his freedom from this absurd marriage, he intends to marry me. Surely you must have realised that?'

'But what about Darrell?'

'He won't stand in my way. He's a good sort and he knows I want more from life than he can give me.'

Perry felt she was being pushed further and further away from Tarquin. But why should she be so deeply hurt? He wanted to be rid of her, didn't he? He had never disguised the fact. But she felt surprised at Lorraine's matter of fact reaction to the news of the marriage.

'Didn't the fact that Tarquin and I had been married come as a shock to you?' she asked now.

'Not really.' Lorraine tossed her head and the black curtain of hair swung away in a graceful curve. 'You see I knew about it.'

'You knew?'

'Yes. Those letters you wrote. I was in charge of Tarquin's correspondence while he was ill. He was in no fit state to be worried with them. He'd forgotten about you entirely. You see you can never have meant very much to him, can you, or why would you have vanished from his memory like that?'

'But you ... you deliberately withheld my letters from him?'

'Of course.'

Lorraine did not look in the least disconcerted at Perry's shocked tone.

'I had to think of what was best for him. What good would it have done to tell him he had a wife whom he couldn't even remember? And how was I to know the marriage was legal anyway? You yourself said in the letters that you had your doubts.'

Perry remembered now all the bitter anguish that she had poured out in those girlish letters, how she had asserted her love, begged him to take some notice of her entreaties, and it had all been wasted on Lorraine. She felt deeply humiliated to think that they had fallen into Lorraine's hands, Lorraine who seemed devoid of any sympathy. Well, she and Tarquin should suit each other if lack of feeling was anything to go by. She must try to forget the love she had thought she had felt yesterday. He was going to marry Lorraine. He had made love to her, Perry, because she was there and there had been no feeling except physical need as far as he was concerned. She couldn't love a man like that. She must learn to hate him.

It was an awkward kind of dinner party. Lorraine was the only one to show any kind of vivacity and she kept the conversation going, concentrating on charming Sinclair while the other two men were for the most part silent. Darrell was even quieter than usual. Did he know already what fate was in store for him? Perry felt very sorry for him because he obviously adored his wife, in spite of her seemingly heartless behaviour. Sinclair was not quite his usual urbane self. The odd noises of the wilderness, the screaming of the baboons, the distant cough of a leopard, the witchlike cackling of hyenas, seemed to repel rather than intrigue him. He started visibly when there was any sudden noise and Perry saw Tarquin's mouth twitch into a mocking grin whenever this happened. Oh, how glad I shall be when I've gone from this place, she thought. But I can never marry Sinclair now. What's to become of me?

'Lorraine has kindly offered me a bed at her house,' Sinclair told Perry when they rose to go. She was surprised remembering how Lorraine had said she could not be bothered with visitors, but she probably enjoyed having a male visitor to stay rather than a female.

'Sorry about this, but I feel I can't stay under that man's roof,' Sinclair told Perry when they were alone for a moment. 'You're quite safe, I take it, since you told me he dislikes you?'

'Perfectly safe, Sinclair,' she assured him. 'After all, I've been staying here for some days now.'

'Feeling about him as I do, I can't accept his hospitality.

Anyhow, we'll be gone tomorrow and you need never return to this dreadful place.'

'No, I needn't, need I?'

Perry stood on the patio that was high above the tree-tops while Tarquin went to speed the visitors on their way. No, she would never come back here, never see again this moonlit pool with its waterlilies luminous in the silvery light, never again hear the splash of that nyala bull having a late long slow drink, beautiful with its curved yellow-tipped horns, black coat and tawny legs. She must go to her room, go before Tarquin came back here, but she lingered, loath to leave the scene, watching a group of crested guinea-fowl chasing each other in circles and then a black-backed jackal coming down to the edge of the pool for a drink.

She turned to go, but it was too late. Tarquin was standing motionless watching her, and, as she saw his dark frown in the lamplight, her heart began to throb painfully. He strode across to her and seized her in the bruising grasp of his strong arms, his wild golden eyes only inches away from her own.

'You lied to me! You've lied to me all along. Why did you say there was no one waiting for you when all the time you knew very well that this lover of yours was just biding his time until you got your freedom from me?'

'He is not my lover! I didn't even know he was going to come here.'

'A likely story when he couldn't even wait until you returned. Tell me, is it as much a disappointment to him as it is to me to find out that this marriage was legal?'

Perry flinched away from his fierce expression. He still held her close, but now his arms were around her and she could feel his hands hard and demanding on the thin fabric of her dress.

'He says, as you do, that we must take the necessary steps to dissolve the marriage,' Perry told him.

It was all she could do to speak clearly. His touch, and the feeling of those sensuous lips so close to her own, were sending her mad. She told herself she hated him now and yet her body was drowning in waves of sweet, insane desire.

'So he intends to marry you? You surprise me. I wouldn't have thought he was the right kind of guy for you.'

All the time he was speaking, his hands were touching her body and she could feel the blood pounding in her veins seeming at fever heat.

'And I suppose you think you are?' she retorted.

'Certainly you must have thought so at one time. Has your taste changed so much in five years?'

She could see his lips so close to hers, but they were parted in that cruel smile and she tried to draw away from him, yet still he held her closely.

'Yes, it has,' she replied breathlessly. 'I was very young when I first met you and I must have been mad to be attracted to you then.'

'Indeed? And what about three nights ago? Or don't you want to be reminded of it? Come, Perry, you can't deny you wanted me then as much as I wanted you.'

'That was folly. It should never have happened.'

'And I suppose this shouldn't be happening either.'

His hand was at her neck and she could feel his long strong fingers lifting the weight of her hair and caressing the sensitive nape. Then the pressure of his hand increased and he drew her face towards his. His mouth came down, smoothing her skin with his open lips until he reached her own. She felt herself going beyond conscious thought. She needed him in the same desperate way that he needed her, but he belonged to Lorraine. This was only an evening's amusement to him, even though she was his legal wife. With a supreme effort of will, she thrust herself away from him.

'You're wrong, Tarquin, I feel nothing but dislike and contempt for you now. I don't know how I could ever have thought I loved you.'

He laughed harshly.

'What in heaven's name has love got to do with this? How typical of a woman to want to bring love into it! I don't believe in love. What we feel for each other is animal desire. Why can't you admit it?'

'No, I won't admit it. I loved you once, but I despise you now. I think you're utterly contemptible!'

And he was, she thought frantically. How could he want to make love to her when he was pledged to Lorraine?

'I'm going back tomorrow and I hope I need never see you again. All our business can be done through solicitors. I should have done that in the first place and I would have been spared the ordeal of the last few days.'

'Ordeal? Is that what you call it? That's odd. I had the impression that part of this ordeal was most enjoyable.'

'Then you had the wrong impression. Please let me go. I can't bear to be with you any longer. You've ruined my life once. Now all I want is to be left alone.'

His frown was dark, but his tone of voice still mocked her.

'Certainly, Mrs Winslow. What a waste of our last hours together! But don't bother to lock your door. You've made your opinion of me very clear. From tomorrow we'll go our separate ways and I hope, like you, that we need never meet again.'

CHAPTER ELEVEN

SOME weeks later, as Perry walked in a London park, the new grass looked astonishingly emerald green to her after the dusty brown of Africa and scores of yellow daffodils with their fresh sharp scent reminded her that here it was almost spring, but yet she would have exchanged it all for one swift glimpse of that other continent with its heat and dust. She would never see Tarquin again, she was sure. He had let her go out of his life without even a farewell and she had spent these weeks in vain regret that theirs had been such a bitter parting.

Too early for her lunch appointment with Sinclair, she had come into the park to walk a little and get her thoughts into some sort of order before having to face him with what she had to tell him. No sooner had they returned than he had had to go away for more than a month, so she had had no opportunity for any kind of serious conversation with him. Did he still have some idea of marrying her when all this legal business had been concluded? But Perry knew now that that was impossible and it would be better if they parted. Yet she dreaded having to tell him. Tarquin had said he would consult his solicitor immediately, that, since the marriage had been in his country, it would be simpler for him to start proceedings, but so far she had heard nothing from him, though every morning she was afraid to look at her post.

As she entered the foyer of the hotel, Sinclair rose from

one of the blue velvet chairs surrounding the ornate little gilt tables and came towards her.

'Perdita, how good to see you again, and in civilised surroundings this time!'

'Very civilised,' Perry agreed, glancing around at the walls of rose-red damask, the velvet curtains with their heavy swags of silken cord, the glittering chandeliers that replaced the early spring sunlight outside. 'Are we celebrating something, Sinclair?'

And then she wished she had not said it, but Sinclair merely laughed, saying, 'Your release from bondage, perhaps?'

'You are looking particularly lovely today,' he told her as he slipped the cream cashmere coat from her shoulders.

She was wearing a dress of a lighter cream, simply cut. The slightly padded shoulders emphasised her tiny waist with its wide belt of soft cyclamen leather, the same colour as the tiny pillbox hat with its swathed veiling that enhanced rather than hid the glorious dark blue of her wide eyes. Her light gold hair was swept into a chignon and the whole effect, down to the champagne-coloured high-heeled shoes with their slender intricate straps, was one of sophistication and elegant charm.

'Rather different from my first sight of you as you returned from that trip into the wilderness. You looked utterly exhausted then. I should never have let you go back to face that ordeal alone.'

'Perhaps I shouldn't have gone, but it's too late now. How different everything would have been if that time in Africa last month had never happened,' Perry told him.

'I agree it was most unfortunate that you felt you had to meet that brute again, most unwise. But not to worry. Nothing has changed, and as soon as the legal business is over you can forget he ever existed. Let's forget about him now at any rate and concentrate on choosing our meal.'

If it were only as simple as Sinclair says, thought Perry. As she heard him ordering the lunch with his usual precise care, she thought, I can't tell him yet that I want to break up with him. How can I? She dreaded and yet looked forward to the time when he would want to discuss the future. She wanted to feel free of him and yet she knew he would be shocked when she told him the reason. But she could not go on with Sinclair, feeling the way she did about Tarquin.

The crisis came, as she had thought it would, when they were seated on the dark blue velvet chairs and the waiter had discreetly served their coffee upon the pretty gilt table with its curling legs decorated with gold cherubs.

'I'm amazed that you should be looking so beautiful, Perdita, after the harrowing experiences of the last few weeks, one would hardly have thought that torrid climate could do anyone any good, but here you are looking more lovely than I've ever seen you.'

'It's kind of you to say that, Sinclair.'

'But it's true. You look adorable. Perdita, I hesitate to make any plans for the future until all this foolish entanglement is cleared away, but you must know how much I admire you. I hope, when it's all over, you will still think that a life that includes me is possible.'

'Oh, Sinclair, you know I've always valued your friendship.'

Perry wanted desperately to avoid what she was almost sure was coming.

'I don't only want that, Perdita. You would make a wonderful wife for a man in my position. Perhaps it's indiscreet to plan anything yet, but in a few months' time I hope you can consider marrying me.'

Sinclair's usually pale face was mottled pink with the nearest to emotion that she had ever seen in him. Perry felt desperately sorry for him, but there was no way to soften the fact that she felt she must refuse him.

'What can I say, Sinclair? It's good of you to want me to be your wife, but I just can't. It's not possible. There's no way it could happen. Everything has changed for me since I went to Africa.'

Sinclair looked stunned.

'What do you mean? Why can't you marry me? How have things changed?'

'I found when I'd been with him for some time that I was still in love with Tarquin. I could never marry anyone else.'

Sinclair brought his hand down on the table making the fragile coffee cups tremble and the little gilt legs shake. Perry thought that she had never before seen him do anything even approaching violence.

'I should never have let you go. I suppose I might have known what would happen, but I trusted you completely. But you must be just imagining this. How could you possibly be attracted to a man like that? I would never have thought you could be taken in by his sort.'

She felt a flare of indignation and knew she was being unfair.

'I'm so sorry I've hurt you, Sinclair. What can I say?'

'You can say you'll reconsider this. What's to happen now? Do you intend to go back to him and not have the marriage dissolved?'

'No, I can never do that. You don't understand, Sinclair. He doesn't love me as I love him. He doesn't even know of my feelings.'

'Now this is absolute nonsense. Do you mean to say you can love him when he means to discard you again? You must be crazy, Perdita!'

'I suppose I am,' said Perry miserably.

'Tell me, did this brute make love to you? Did he force himself on you?'

'No, it wasn't like that, but I admit there is this terrific physical attraction between us. I suppose there always has been.'

Tears came to her eyes, but she brushed them aside. She had done enough weeping on her own in the lonely hours of the night during the last few weeks.

'Truly I've tried to hate him. I know I should, and he doesn't feel in any way attached to me, but the way I still feel about him I could never consider marrying anyone else.'

Sinclair's features looked pinched.

'I never dreamed you could be so impulsive, so uncontrolled in your emotions, Perdita. Oh, you'd told me about this early mishap, but I blamed your innocence and Tarquin's wiles, but now I don't know what to think. Perhaps I never knew you properly. I respected and admired the person I thought you were. You were always so cool, so restrained, so ladylike, but now it seems I was wrong.'

'I think you were, Sinclair. It would be a mistake for us to marry. You need a different kind of woman from me. I must go out of your life. It's best we shouldn't meet again. There's no point in continuing our friendship.'

'But surely this is only a temporary thing,' he persisted. 'If you could get over this mad attraction the man has for you, you would see that life with me would be a much sounder possibility than anything Tarquin could offer you. And it doesn't make sense anyway, since you've told me you still mean to go ahead with the divorce.'

'I have to. He can't wait to get free in order to marry Lorraine. She told me so herself.'

'Wait until the divorce is through, then we'll talk about this once more. You'll see, away from that so called glamorous background, you'll soon learn to forget him.'

'No, Sinclair, you must understand—you've been kind to me always, but now I feel we should part.'

'Now you're being too hard on me and on yourself. Admittedly it might be discreet if we stopped seeing quite so much of each other until the divorce is through, but after that I'll feel myself free to ask you the same question again, and I'm sure next time I'll get a different answer.'

Oh, why was he so obstinate?

'Sinclair, please try to understand. You'll never get a different answer. I just know it isn't possible now.'

She offered to take a taxi back to her apartment, but he insisted on driving her home in his sleek silver-grey Jaguar. She did not ask him to come in, fearing more argument, but he detained her on the pavement in an attempt to make her see reason. He talked very eloquently, putting his arms around her shoulders as if he were afraid she would slip away from him, trying to convince her that they should still stay together. To all his arguments she smiled and shook her head, and at last he seemed to accept that he was not to see her again. He had been good to her in his own way, she thought, and he could not help being Sinclair. Perhaps she had been wrong in allowing him to hope too much, but certainly now she felt it was all over between them. She leaned forward and kissed him, feeling that now this really was goodbye, and he, a little more moved than usual, put his arms around her, saying, 'Remember my advice, Perdita, forget this man and don't be foolish.'

He kissed her again, then turned and drove away as she entered the foyer of the small block of apartments. She was feeling rather upset and wanted to get to her room quickly, but as she hurried in the direction of the elevator, a man rose from his seat in the lobby and came towards her. She gasped as she recognised the tall, bronzed figure.

'Tarquin!'

'Don't look so astonished, Perry. It's merely a business visit. I called to get your signature on some papers. Don't look at me as if I'm a visitor from Mars.'

'But you might as well be. I couldn't be more surprised. What on earth are you doing in London?'

Could he see the way her heart was thudding under the thin fabric of the cream dress? she wondered. Oh, how could she have this exultant feeling of utter joy when she knew he could not possibly feel the same?

'I've come to deliver some white rhinos to a private zoo. We don't often send them by air and they had to be thoroughly tranquillised and needed careful supervision. It was quite an anxious trip, I can tell you. But we've got them here safely now and I took the opportunity of coming to see you about this legal procedure. I haven't got it going properly yet, but the solicitor seems to think it should be fairly straightforward. Are you going to ask me up to your apartment?'

'Of course.'

She had been standing staring at him as if indeed he had been a visitor from outer space, and now she turned with him towards the elevator. Closed in by the small cubicle, she felt almost suffocated by the force of her emotions. He was wearing a dark suit and yet he looked utterly alien to the London scene, so large, so powerful, his craggy features and strong hands so bronzed and such a contrast to the immaculate white of his shirt. His eyes, golden and glowing, were as watchful as those of a lion who is stalking his prey. She could not believe she had ever known the kisses of that sensuous mouth with its bitter expression.

Her apartment in this great block was high above London's traffic like a bird's nest in a very tall tree. The tiny all-purpose room held a divan bed pushed up against the wall with a sprigged duvet upon it and matching cushions, one easy chair and a small desk. There was a minute bathroom which doubled as a kitchen. The window came down to the ground level and there was a wide view even as far as St Paul's and the river. Tarquin, with his tall frame and powerful shoulders, seemed far too large for his surroundings. He took one stride towards the window and his expression relaxed into a kind of smile.

'Somewhat like being in an eagle's nest but far more confined,' he commented. 'How in heaven's name can you live like this? But I suppose it suits you.'

Perry wanted to tell him that it didn't suit her, that, after being in Africa, she knew that city life was not for her and that she longed to come back, but she could never say this to him because he had started the wheels of law rolling in order to marry Lorraine and he had no feeling for her, Perry, anyway. She knew that when he left she would suffer terrible anguish again and she wished desperately that he had not come here because now she would be able to visualise him not as before against the background of Africa but here in this little room, looking immense and very male among the Victorian prints, the sprigged Laura Ashley wallpaper and fabrics that decorated it.

'You're still involved with this man, I see,' he remarked.

'What man?'

Tarquin's sudden appearance had put everything else out of her head. It was as if the lunch with Sinclair had taken place in a previous existence.

'This ... what's his name? ... Sinclair, don't you call him? You presented a very affectionate picture when you were parting at the door. I suppose he can't wait to marry you. Are you still looking forward to it, Perry?'

'No, not exactly,' she stammered, and hastened to add, 'I mean, I can't think of anything like that until ...'

'Until you're free. Well, it may not take too long. You'd better sign these couple of papers while we think about it.'

He put the documents on the desk and Perry signed them obediently, not even bothering to read them for she felt, if she did so, her hardwon control might snap and she might burst into tears. She was dreadfully conscious of his close presence in the little room and, as he bent over the desk to indicate where she should sign, she was aware of the musky fragrance of his body underneath the civilised veneer of his city clothes. That large brown hand, that was near her own as she signed her name, had caressed her once, but she must not think of it. She must put it right out of her mind.

As she finished signing her name, she felt his eyes upon her. She straightened up from the desk and turned her back to him, gazing out of the window and fighting for control, but she sensed his dark presence near to her and, as he put his hands on her shoulders, his touch seemed to send a flame through her body. He drew her towards him, but she told herself she dared not respond to those compelling hands, although he was so close now that she could feel the hardness of his chest muscles, sense the beat of his heart as if it were throbbing in her own breast.

With a flick of his fingers he had removed the elegant hat and she felt his mouth on the nape of her neck where the blonde curls escaped from the smooth coiffure.

'And Perry, we have some unfinished business, haven't we?'

His questing hand was on the tender milky skin of her neck and she felt the zip of her dress run smoothly down the length of her back. His hands were smoothing her upper arms, reaching to the wisps of lace that enclosed the curves of her breasts. She turned, but as his head came down to seek her mouth, she twisted away from him.

'How can you? You've just seen me sign the papers that will help you regain your freedom and yet you think you can use me like this. Oh, you're despicable! I've never known anyone else with your particular brand of arrogance. How can even you dare to treat me like this?'

'Why not? You attract me physically—you must know that. I thought we attracted each other. Correct me if I'm

wrong. But anything else is out of the question, obviously.
Look at you—your mode of dressing, your expensive perfume that even now is driving me wild. No, Perry, you must
realise that we're totally unsuited to each other. I simply
can't imagine you as you look now living in Africa, and yet
there's this physical rapport between us. What's so bad
about that? And why should we not take advantage of this
short time together?'

'Because I have no intention of doing so. And you're
wrong about our being attracted to each other. I hope
that after today I never see you again!'

'So you really intend to marry this Sinclair? I wouldn't
have believed that a girl with as much spirit as you could
be attracted to a twit like that if I hadn't seen it with my
own eyes. Tell me, do you enjoy those mild-as-milk kisses?
Does it feed your ego to be treated with such grovelling
respect?'

'It's better than being used!' Perry flung out, goaded to
fury by the sight of his mocking mouth and the flashing
scorn of his golden eyes.

'I wish you joy of him, then. Goodbye, Perry, but let me
remind you first how it feels to be properly kissed.'

She was in his arms now and she felt again the steel-like
hardness of his body as he kissed her savagely and completely. She reminded herself how much she should hate
him, and yet she felt waves of ecstasy trembling through
her lower limbs. But as she felt herself wildly responding to
his searching mouth, he flung her aside. She felt herself
falling backwards on to the bed and heard the door slam
shut.

Oh, how could he be so cruel as to discard her? She
could not bear the thought that she would never see him
again. She would follow him, tell him that she loved him.
What did pride matter beside the feeling that she had for
him now?

As she hesitated, she heard the elevator door open and then shut, and knew she must get to him before he disappeared once more from her life. Opening the door, she ran along the corridor to the fire escape and started clambering down the precipitous steps. She tried not to look down, but she could not avoid the view of London that swung dizzily below her.

Faster, she must go faster, if she were to intercept him before he left the building! Oh, here were the last few steps winding to the bottom and she could look down to the ground now. Surely she would be in time to meet him! And then, just above street level, her high-heeled elegant shoe caught in a rung of the curving stairway and she was pitched violently forward on to the hard pavement.

CHAPTER TWELVE

STRANGERS had picked her up unconscious and taken her to the casualty ward of a nearby hospital, there she was X-rayed and treated for bad bruising and shock. But she was not seriously hurt. Now she knew it had been crazy to feel she should pursue Tarquin that day, for he had walked out of her life without even a backward glance and did not even know what had happened to her.

Some weeks had passed and yet she had heard nothing further about the legal proceedings for the dissolution of the marriage, but she supposed these things took time. It did not make any difference to her life anyway. Even though she would be technically free she would never marry anyone else.

By now spring had advanced and the world looked sparkling and new, the skies washed blue by sudden showers. Flowers appeared in window boxes; dresses in fresh light colours were in the boutiques. But all this promise of new life seemed to mock her present state of mind. Now she felt condemned to a blank kind of half life. She could not recover from the despair that seized her when she thought she could never hope to see Tarquin again.

Before she went to Africa she had given up her job with a magazine and, on her return, she had taken freelance work, thinking she would not be doing it for many more months, for she wanted to get away from London. It was rather an impersonal way of living and she made no friends. She had lost touch with her previous acquaintances and had not the desire or energy to renew these slight ties, so at night she stayed in her little room, dreaming of Africa, gazing at the huge panorama of dancing lights but seeing in her mind's eye the shimmering lake, the white pelicans flying far from the shore, the pink clouds of flamingoes rising from the reeds, the hippos grazing at the edge.

Then one day, when she arrived home in the evening, the supervisor of the apartment building called to her as she collected her post.

'Hello, Miss Vaughan, there was a guy asking after you, a big man, very suntanned. Kind of foreigner, I'd say.'

Tarquin! No, it couldn't be.

'Did he give any name?' she asked.

'No, but he said he'd be back.'

It couldn't be Tarquin, she thought, as she hastily showered and changed into slacks and a T-shirt. This time she wouldn't be caught out giving an impression of immense sophistication. But what was she thinking of? Tarquin would never come back after that final scene. It was all over between them. But when the phone rang and the supervisor said there was someone to see her, she could scarcely control her trembling. She opened the door, her heart hurting in her breast, then she let out a long sigh, half relief, half disappointment.

'Darrell! Good heavens, I never expected to see you here!'

'Nor I you, Perry, but I thought I'd look in. I had to come to see to the rhinos Tarquin brought over. They've been having a few problems and the zoo owners paid my fare to come over and sort them out.'

'How exciting for you. Won't you sit down? Would you like a cup of tea?'

'Thanks, that would be great.'

Her heart had steadied down now and she could speak normally. Of course, she told herself, she had known it couldn't be Tarquin. It was kind of Darrell to look her up. She was a fool to have this blank horrible let-down feeling. But once she had made tea, she couldn't help wanting to bring Tarquin's name into the conversation.

'How was it that you came instead of Tarquin?' she asked.

Darrell, his large hand enveloping the bone china cup, stared at her blankly.

'But Tarquin is here.'

'You mean you both came together?'

'No, of course not. Tarquin has been here since he brought the rhinos over. I thought you would have known that.'

'Here, in London? No, I didn't.'

Tarquin was here in London and she had not known. Yet how could she? He had not even been interested enough to get in touch with her again. But how could he have done after that last scene?

'But why has he stayed here all this time?' she asked.

Darrell looked enormously confused.

'Maybe I wasn't supposed to tell you. I haven't seen him yet. I'm to see him tomorrow. They ration the number of visitors he has. I think in fact that I'll be the first.'

'Visitors? Darrell, please tell me, what are you talking about?'

'I really thought you knew. Tarquin's in hospital. He didn't just come to bring those rhinos, but to have an operation to remove some pressure from his brain.'

Perry gasped.

'A brain operation—but isn't that very dangerous?'

'Yes, it was, but the doctors said it was more risky to leave it. You know it had changed his personality some-what, making him easily angered and irritable, and another thing, he couldn't stand the idea of having those blanks in his memory. He was told that this op might do the trick.'

'And did it?'

'That I don't know. I'll find out when I see him tomorrow.'

'But, Darrell,' Perry cried, 'you haven't told me anything. How is he? When did he have the operation? Is he very ill?'

'He was. It was touch and go for quite a few days, I believe. Most people would have passed out with all he's gone through, but he's a tough guy, is old Tarquin, strong as an ox. In fact, he's hoping to come back with me when I go. Whether they'll let him remains to be seen.'

'So that's why I didn't hear anything more about the separation,' Perry murmured almost to herself.

'Yes, well, I suppose all that business got slowed down because of Tarquin's illness. Tell me, Perry, are you still determined to go through with it?'

'What choice do I have? Tarquin doesn't care for me any more, if he ever did.'

'And I understand you're going to marry the man who arrived to fetch you.'

'No, Darrell, I'm not. But it doesn't make any difference. Tarquin thinks I'm going to marry Sinclair, but what does it matter? In any case, he's never regarded me as his wife. He didn't even know of my existence until a few weeks ago.'

Weeks in which so much had happened, but Lorraine's name had not come up in the conversation and Perry was not going to be the first to mention it.

'Perry,' said Darrell, sounding rather embarrassed, 'you're his wife. You do care for him—I could see that when I told you about his operation. You looked absolutely stricken. I think the least you can do is to go and see Tarquin. He's been pretty ill and surely you must want to see him before he goes back. Come with me tomorrow when I visit him.'

Perry shook her head. She was dying to see Tarquin. Indeed, her first impulse had been to rush to the hospital straight away, but something held her back.

Darrell said hesitantly, 'You think he loves Lorraine, don't you? Is that what's worrying you?'

Perry felt confused by Darrell's frankness. What could she say?

'You mustn't take any notice of what Lorraine says. She's inclined to exaggerate. She has a vivid imagination at times and gets carried away by it sometimes. She's known Tarquin for so long now that she's jealous of any other woman who has anything to do with him. She has this possessive nature, in fact sometimes she seems to think she owns him, but, Perry, I assure you we have no intention of breaking up. Tarquin is my friend. I trust him completely.'

Can this be true, Perry wondered, or is it just what Darrell wants to believe?

'I think you should come with me tomorrow,' Darrell went on, 'then you'll satisfy yourself about Tarquin's condition.'

'I don't think he'll want to see me.'

'If he doesn't want to see you, he can always say so.'

'Maybe you're right. Oh, very well, I'll come.'

I've endured enough humiliation at Tarquin's hands, Perry thought, so what does one more time matter? If, as Darrell suggested, he was going to turn her away, she could not surely be made more sad about him than she was already. And, in her heart, she knew that she was leaping at the chance of seeing him again, and that now she knew he had been ill, she would never be satisfied until she could reassure herself about his condition.

Next day, when they stood at the reception desk of the small private clinic where Tarquin had had the operation, the nursing Sister looked at Perry doubtfully.

'We aren't keen on too many visitors for Mr Winslow. I said you could visit him because after all you've come from Africa and are his assistant, but I'm not sure whether Matron would approve of my letting in anyone else.'

'Miss Vaughan is his . . . I mean, she's a close personal friend of Mr Winslow's. I'm sure he would want to see her,' said Darrell.

For a shocked moment Perry had feared Darrell was going to tell the Sister that she was Tarquin's wife and she could not have borne that for it would have led to many awkward questions.

'Oh, very well, but you must go in one at time and don't stay more than five minutes.'

It was odd to think that she was going to see Tarquin in this bare shining place smelling faintly of disinfectant. It was the last place in the world where she would have expected to visit him.

'A visitor for you, Mr Winslow,' the nurse announced, and Perry was left alone to traverse what seemed yards of gleaming floor to the high bed that seemed too narrow and small to hold Tarquin. His head was bandaged and his face showed bronze against the white of the dressings, but the ruddy colour had gone from his cheeks.

'Perry, what the hell are you doing here?'

He sounded shocked. What had she been hoping for? That perhaps the operation had restored his memory of that earlier, happier time and he could learn to love her once more?

'Darrell brought me here. I didn't know before he came that you've been ill.'

'And you weren't meant to know. Darrell is an interfering swine.'

'He thought I ought to know,' Perry told him.

'In heaven's name, why? Why did you come? I suppose

you want to know why the legal proceedings have been delayed? Though why you're panting to marry that milksop Sinclair, I just can't imagine.'

She longed to touch one of the large hands that lay there so brown against the white coverlet. If she could establish any kind of communication, surely he would not go on staring at her with that fierce golden gaze like a lion intimidating its prey?

'Was the operation a success?' she persisted. 'Has it restored your memory?'

'It was a success, I suppose, in that the pressure on the brain has been removed and the danger to my life has passed, but no, if you think I've remembered anything that happened in the past, you're mistaken. Everything is as it was before, and as soon as I can get things going when I return home, you can be assured you'll get your freedom. Now go, please, Perry. There's no place for us in each other's lives now. I'll be much happier if I need never see you again.'

She had stumbled past Darrell murmuring that she would take a taxi back to the apartment, and had ignored his protests and his pleas that she should wait for him. And now a week had passed, a week in which she had gone backwards and forwards to her work in a daze of misery. When her present job was finished, she decided, she would take some time off, go right away to some small place, perhaps to the Lake District, where she could walk and try to forget about Tarquin and Africa. He must have gone by now, she thought, because Darrell had said they were to go together and she had not heard anything further from him.

Today at lunchtime she had walked in the park. The sun was warm and amidst the blossoming trees lovers were lying on the newly green grass, completely absorbed in each other. Perry's heart ached with pain when she saw them. I'm scarcely twenty-three years old, she thought, and I'll

...ver love again because I'll never get over this feeling I have for Tarquin.

In the evening, back in her little room, she had a shower and changed into a pale yellow gown of fine lawn trimmed with white broderie anglaise edging and flowers embroidered in pastel colours. Full sleeves were caught into the wrists and the low neckline half revealed her small high breasts. The mirror gave her a reflection of a girl with hair almost the same colour as the pretty gown and eyes of dark forget-me-not blue. Tarquin had said once that she was beautiful. So why, now, did he seem to hate her so? Don't think about him, she told herself. But how can I help it?

The bell at her door rang sharp and shrill. Who could be coming to see her at this hour? Maybe it was someone come to the wrong door. It was on a chain and she opened it cautiously.

Tarquin! His hair was short and curly where it had been shorn and he was paler than usual, a little haggard as if he had lost weight, but Tarquin, looking at her with an expression she found hard to understand.

'Are you going to unfasten this chain?' he asked. 'Or am I to be barred out of your life for ever?'

She had been gazing at him through the slit of the doorway as if her eyes were somehow deceiving her, but now she slid the chain off its hook.

'Perry, don't look so shattered. I had to come to see you before I left.'

'You mean you want more papers signed.'

He seemed to fill the little room and she had a wild sensation of panic. She mustn't let him know how much his mere presence meant to her.

'Oh, to hell with signing papers! No, Perry, I came to see you, though I can't help thinking that I'm probably too late.'

'Too late?' he queried.

'Is it too late, Perry?'

'I don't understand.'

Though it seemed to her the harshness had somehow disappeared from his voice, she would not look at his face because she feared she might see that aloof expression and that this was just another incident to add to her hurt. She walked over to the window, turning her back on him.

But he was there behind her, holding her closely, his lips brushing against her hair.

'I lied to you, Perry. I was mad with rage and jealousy because I was sure you meant to marry Sinclair and I thought after the last time we met that you hated me.'

She turned towards him and saw unbelievingly that his golden eyes had lost their wild ferocity and his expression was warm, even tender.

'How did you lie to me?' she asked.

'I told you that my memory hadn't returned, but it had, Perry. I remember those lovely days we spent together. I remember how we felt about each other. I remember that I was afraid of losing you because you were so young and that's why I felt we must keep it secret until we could choose a time to tell your family.'

'But if you remembered that, why did you tell me the operation had failed?'

'I thought it was best for me to get out of your life for ever because you seemed so determined to marry Sinclair. Your whole life seemed organised for staying here. I thought my kind of life could never suit you. And then Darrell told me that you had no intention of marrying Sinclair and he even implied that I might have a chance. Tell me the truth, Perry, have I? After all this time, could you learn to love me again?'

Even though his expression was pleading, his eyes tender and loving, she could not believe what she was hearing.

'But ... but I thought you intended to marry Lorraine.'

'Lorraine? Good heavens, no! How could you think such a thing? I could never steal a friend's wife. She's been a good friend to me, useful in organising the household, but she's inclined to take advantage of our long acquaintance to become rather possessive. I'll miss Darrell, but it's a good thing they're going.'

'Going?' she queried.

'Yes, Darrel has been put in charge of another game reserve in another part of Africa and his health is much improved now. They're going there immediately. But you haven't answered my question—or are you avoiding it? Answer me, Perry, answer me now. Could you possibly learn to love me again?'

There was a desperate urgency in his tones, but the arrogance had gone. And now his hand was at the curve of her waist, his mouth moving against her cheek.

'You loved me once, Perry. Have I any chance of recovering that love? Please say you'll try to forget I was such a brute when I met you again. I've sometimes been hardly responsible for my bad moods, but the doctors assure me the cause of them has passed.'

She put her hand on his neck where the short chestnut curls were growing again and brought his mouth down towards hers.

'I don't have to try. Oh, Tarquin, I do love you so very much. I tried not to, but it was no use. I think I've loved you since the first day I met you and I've never stopped even through all those years of separation.'

She was clinging to him now like someone who has been lost for a long time in the dark, but now his kisses were bringing her back into the light.

'What a waste of years,' he muttered as he kissed her.

Some time later he asked her, 'Perry, don't you hate the idea of living in Africa? After all, you're used to a much more sophisticated life. That day I came here before, I'd made up my mind to ask you to give our marriage a try, but when I saw you being so affectionate to Sinclair, and when I saw how elegantly you were dressed, I thought it was no go, and that you could never come back with me to Africa. That is why I tried so desperately to make love to you because I thought I would never have another chance.'

'I was saying goodbye to Sinclair that day—that's why we were kissing. And, Tarquin, I've longed all these years to come back. There's nothing I want more.'

His lips were on her face now and he was kissing her gently at first but with growing passion.

'I love you, Perry, even more than I did when you were first my wife in that little African village that's disappeared. May I stay with you now in your small eyrie, or do you want me to go?'

'Oh, no, don't go. Don't ever leave me again.'

'Lovely Perry, tomorrow we'll book our flight home, but tonight is all ours.'

The desperation had gone from their kisses and they touched each other slowly and gently, knowing that they were to have a whole lifetime in which to enjoy their love.

Here's how to get your volume NOW!

MAIL IN	$	GET
2 SPECIAL PROOF-OF-PURCHASE SEALS*	**PLUS $1 U.S.**	**ONE BOOK**
5 SPECIAL PROOF-OF-PURCHASE SEALS*	**PLUS 50¢ U.S.**	**ONE BOOK**
8 SPECIAL PROOF-OF-PURCHASE SEALS*	**FREE**	**ONE BOOK**

*Special proof-of-purchase seal from inside back cover of all specially marked Harlequin "Let Your Imagination Fly Sweepstakes" volumes. No other proof-of-purchase accepted.

ORDERING DETAILS:

Print your name, address, city, state or province, zip or postal code on the coupon below or a plain 3"x 5" piece of paper and together with the special proof-of-purchase seals and check or money order (no stamps or cash please) as indicated. Mail to:

**HARLEQUIN
ROMANCE TREASURY
BOOK OFFER
P.O. BOX 1399
MEDFORD, N.Y. 11763, U.S.A.**

Make check or money order payable to: Harlequin Romance Treasury Offer. Allow 3 to 4 weeks for delivery.

Special offer expires: June 30, 1981.

PLEASE PRINT

Name

Address

Apt. No.

City

State/ Prov.

Zip/Postal Code

Let Your Imagination Fly Sweepstakes

Rules and Regulations:

NO PURCHASE NECESSARY

1. Enter the Let Your Imagination Fly Sweepstakes 1, 2 or 3 as often as you wish. Mail each entry form separately bearing sufficient postage. Specify the sweepstake you wish to enter on the outside of the envelope. Mail a completed entry form or, your name, address, and telephone number printed on a plain 3"x 5" piece of paper to:
HARLEQUIN LET YOUR IMAGINATION FLY SWEEPSTAKES,
P.O. BOX 1280, MEDFORD, N.Y. 11763 U.S.A.

2. Each completed entry form must be accompanied by 1 Let Your Imagination Fly proof-of-purchase seal from the back inside cover of specially marked Let Your Imagination Fly Harlequin books (or the words "Let Your Imagination Fly" printed on a plain 3"x 5" piece of paper. Specify by number the Sweepstakes you are entering on the outside of the envelope.

3. The prize structure for each sweepstake is as follows:

Sweepstake 1 - North America
Grand Prize winner's choice: a one-week trip for two to either Bermuda; Montreal, Canada; or San Francisco. 3 Grand Prizes will be awarded (min. approx. retail value $1,375. U.S., based on Chicago departure) and 4,000 First Prizes: scarves by nik nik, worth $14. U.S. each. All prizes will be awarded.

Sweepstake 2 - Caribbean
Grand Prize winner's choice: a one-week trip for two to either Nassau, Bahamas; San Juan, Puerto Rico; or St. Thomas, Virgin Islands. 3 Grand Prizes will be awarded. (Min. approx. retail value $1,650. U.S., based on Chicago departure) and 4,000 First Prizes: simulated diamond pendants by Kenneth Jay Lane, worth $15. U.S. each. All prizes will be awarded.

Sweepstake 3 - Europe
Grand Prize winner's choice: a one-week trip for two to either London, England; Frankfurt, Germany; Paris, France; or Rome, Italy. 3 Grand Prizes will be awarded. (Min. approx. retail value $2,800. U.S., based on Chicago departure) and 4,000 First Prizes: 1/2 oz. bottles of perfume, BLAZER by Anne Klein. (Retail value over $30. U.S.). All prizes will be awarded.

Grand trip prizes will include coach round-trip airfare for two persons from the nearest commercial airport serviced by Delta Air Lines to the city as designated in the prize, double occupancy accommodation at a first-class or medium hotel, depending on vacation, and $500. U.S. spending money. Departure taxes, visas, passports, ground transportation to and from airports will be the responsibility of the winners.

4. To be eligible, Sweepstakes entries must be received as follows:
Sweepstake 1 Entries received by February 28, 1981
Sweepstake 2 Entries received by April 30, 1981
Sweepstake 3 Entries received by June 30, 1981
Make sure you enter each Sweepstake separately since entries will not be carried forward from one Sweepstake to the next.

The odds of winning will be determined by the number of entries received in each of the three sweepstakes. Canadian residents, in order to win any prize, will be required to first correctly answer a time-limited skill-testing question, to be posed by telephone, at a mutually convenient time.

5. Random selections to determine Sweepstake 1, 2 or 3 winners will be conducted by Lee Krost Associates, an independent judging organization whose decisions are final. Only one prize per family, per sweepstake. Prizes are non-transferable and non-refundable and no substitutions will be allowed. Winners will be responsible for any applicable federal, state and local taxes. Trips must be taken during normal tour periods before June 30, 1982 Reservations will be on a space-available basis. Airline tickets are non-transferable, non-refundable and non-redeemable for cash.

6. The Let Your Imagination Fly Sweepstakes is open to all residents of the United States of America and Canada, (excluding the Province of Quebec) except employees and their immediate families of Harlequin Enterprises Ltd., its advertising agencies, Marketing & Promotion Group Canada Ltd. and Lee Krost Associates, Inc., the independent judging company. Winners may be required to furnish proof of eligibility. Void wherever prohibited or restricted by law. All federal, state, provincial and local laws apply.

7. For a list of trip winners, send a stamped, self-addressed envelope to:
Harlequin Trip Winners List, P.O. Box 1401, MEDFORD, N.Y. 11763 U.S.A.
Winners lists will be available after the last sweepstake has been conducted and winners determined.
NO PURCHASE NECESSARY

Let Your Imagination Fly Sweepstakes
OFFICIAL ENTRY FORM

Please enter me in Sweepstake No.

Please print:

Name

Address

Apt. No.   City

State/   Zip/Postal
Prov.   Code

Telephone No.   area code
(   )

MAIL TO:
HARLEQUIN LET YOUR
IMAGINATION FLY SWEEPSTAKE No.
P.O. BOX 1280,
MEDFORD, N.Y. 11763 U.S.A.

(Please specify by number, the Sweepstake you are entering.)